W9-AYH-588

THE INTERNATIONAL ENCYCLOPEDIA OF PHYSICAL CHEMISTRY AND CHEMICAL PHYSICS

Topic 1. MATHEMATICAL TECHNIQUES

EDITOR: PROFESSOR H. JONES

Volume 4

MATRICES AND TENSORS

BY

G. G. Hall, M.A., B.Sc., Ph.D.

THE INTERNATIONAL ENCYCLOPEDIA OF PHYSICAL CHEMISTRY AND CHEMICAL PHYSICS

THE INTERNATIONAL ENCYCLOPEDIA OF PHYSICAL CHEMISTRY AND CHEMICAL PHYSICS

MATRICES AND TENSORS

BY

G. G. HALL, M.A., B.Sc., Ph.D.

PROFESSOR OF APPLIED MATHEMATICS IN
THE UNIVERSITY OF NOTTINGHAM

A Pergamon Press Book

THE MACMILLAN COMPANY
NEW YORK
1963

THE MACMILLAN COMPANY
60 Fifth Avenue
New York 11, N.Y.

This book is distributed by
THE MACMILLAN COMPANY · NEW YORK
pursuant to a special arrangement with
PERGAMON PRESS LIMITED
Oxford, England

Library of Congress Card Number 62–22063

**Set in Modern 7—11 on 13pt. by Santype Limited, Salisbury,
and printed in Great Britain by The Pitman Press, Lower Bristol Road, Bath.**

INTRODUCTION

The International Encyclopedia of Physical Chemistry and Chemical Physics is a comprehensive and modern account of all aspects of the domain of science between chemistry and physics, and is written primarily for the graduate and research worker. The Editors-in-Chief, Professor E. A. Guggenheim, Professor J. E. Mayer and Professor F. C. Tompkins, have grouped the subject matter in some twenty groups (General Topics), each having its own editor. The complete work consists of about one hundred volumes, each volume being restricted to around two hundred pages and having a large measure of independence. Particular importance has been given to the exposition of the fundamental bases of each topic and to the development of the theoretical aspects; experimental details of an essentially practical nature are not emphasized although the theoretical background of techniques and procedures is fully developed.

The Encyclopedia is written throughout in English and the recommendations of the International Union of Pure and Applied Chemistry on notation and cognate matters in physical chemistry are adopted. Abbreviations for names of journals are in accordance with *The World List of Scientific Periodicals.*

CONTENTS

PREFACE

THE aim of this book is to provide an account of the theory of vectors, linear equations, matrices and tensors which serves the needs of graduate chemists, physicists or engineers. The first need is for a description of the various entities, their nature and manipulation, and a derivation of the mathematical properties most frequently needed in applications. The second need is for a short selection of efficient methods of solving linear equations and eigenvalue problems, adequate for practical numerical application and described in sufficient detail to be used confidently. These methods should be suitable for hand-calculation and include the information needed to use them on an electronic computer.

In both content and presentation this book is intended to bridge the gap between books and courses designed to introduce the subject to science undergraduates and treatises written for mathematicians. This gap is felt most keenly by those beginning research and facing urgent numerical problems. It is hoped that this account, if not itself sufficient to solve a problem, may give enough background to enable specialized textbooks and journals to be consulted fruitfully. The examples after each chapter have the same purpose. Some provide direct illustrations of the ideas and procedures in the text but others are introductions to more advanced topics or more specialized applications.

The author is happy to be able to acknowledge his debt to many from whose discussion and writing he has profited and, in particular, to Dr. S. F. Boys and Prof. P. O. Löwdin whose experienced judgements have been invaluable, and to his wife for her help in preparing the manuscript and her forbearance during its writing.

CHAPTER 1

VECTORS

1.1 Definitions

The theory of vectors is most easily understood as a theory of arrows drawn from a common point. These arrows can then be used to represent physical properties such as the position, velocity or acceleration of a particle or the displacement of an atom from its equilibrium position in a molecule. The theory enables any such properties, which have a magnitude, a direction and a sense and so can be represented by arrows, to be described by one abstract symbol. The arrows will usually be considered as lying in a three dimensional space although much of the theory is independent of the dimension of the space. The generalization to an n-dimensional space is treated later.

Vectors are represented in diagrams by arrows drawn from an origin and are denoted in the text by lower case letters in distinctive type. The basic operation which can be performed on vectors is known as addition. The sum of two vectors is defined geometrically as the

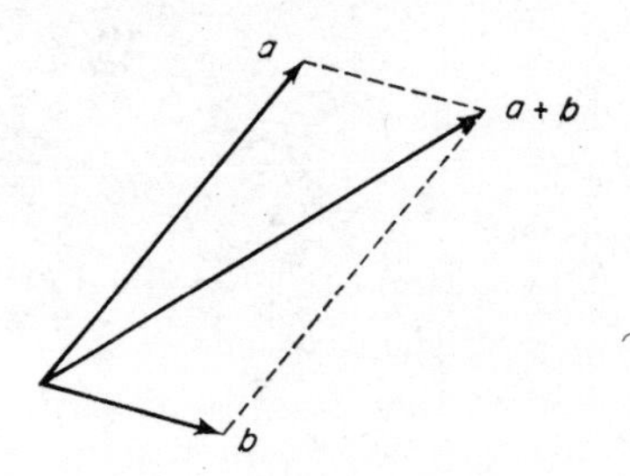

FIG. 1.1. Addition of 2 vectors.

diagonal of the parallelogram formed by the two vectors and two lines drawn parallel to them as in Fig. 1.1. According to this definition it is clear that the sum is independent of the order of addition,

$$a + b = b + a \tag{1.1.1}$$

This process of addition can be continued with any number of vectors by adding them in pairs until a single vector remains. As with ordinary addition, there are various ways of doing this, differing in the order of performing the additions, but these all lead to the same total sum. For three vectors the three ways are indicated by

$$(a + b) + c, \qquad a + (b + c), \qquad (a + c) + b$$

and Fig. 1.2 shows that these are three different methods of specifying the space diagonal of the parallelepiped spanned by the three vectors.

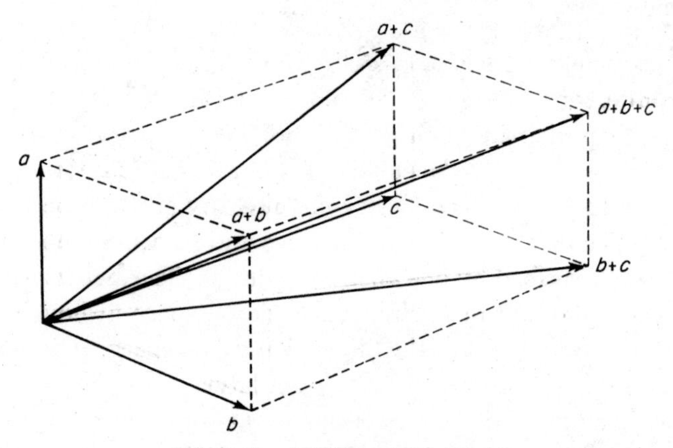

Fig. 1.2. Addition of 3 vectors.

The general result for any number of vectors follows logically from this

Addition leads naturally to subtraction. If

$$a + b = c \tag{1.1.2}$$

then the difference is defined as

$$b = c - a \tag{1.1.3}$$

Figure 1.1 shows that subtraction can be defined geometrically by completing the triangle formed by the two vectors to be subtracted and then this third side, transferred to the origin by drawing parallels, gives the difference. When a vector is subtracted from itself the result is just the origin itself; so this point may be interpreted as a null vector 0 with the properties

$$a - a = 0 \tag{1.1.4}$$

$$a + 0 = a \tag{1.1.5}$$

When a vector is added to itself the result is a vector having the same direction and sense but of twice the length. By generalization of this, any multiple of a vector may be defined as a vector in the same direction as the original vector but with the length magnified by the multiple. Negative multiples are defined similarly but have the sense of the vector reversed. These multiples obviously obey the usual rules of multiplication

$$(\lambda + \mu)a = \lambda a + \mu a \tag{1.1.6}$$

$$\lambda(a + b) = \lambda a + \lambda b \tag{1.1.7}$$

$$\lambda(\mu a) = (\lambda\mu)a \tag{1.1.8}$$

The second of these rules gives a method of stating the similarity of similar triangles.

1.2 Concurrence of Medians

The power of the vector theory is illustrated by the rapid proofs, which it makes possible, of geometrical theorems such as the concurrence of the medians of a triangle. To prove this theorem the origin is taken at a vertex of the triangle and the two adjoining sides are denoted by the vectors a and b (Fig. 1.3). The arrows to the mid-points of these

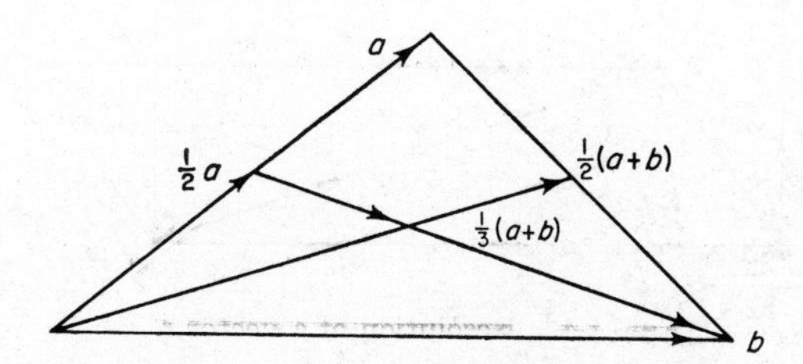

FIG. 1.3. Intersecting medians.

sides are then $\frac{1}{2}a$ and $\frac{1}{2}b$. The median to the third side is then half the diagonal of the parallelogram, viz. $\frac{1}{2}(a + b)$, since the diagonals of a parallelogram bisect one another. Consider now the point $\frac{2}{3}$ along this median viz. $\frac{1}{3}(a + b)$. The vector joining this to $\frac{1}{2}a$ is

$$\tfrac{1}{3}(a + b) - \tfrac{1}{2}a = \tfrac{1}{3}b - \tfrac{1}{6}a \tag{1.2.1}$$

and the vector joining it to the opposite vertex is

$$b - \tfrac{1}{3}(a + b) = \tfrac{2}{3}b - \tfrac{1}{3}a \tag{1.2.2}$$

These two vectors are clearly in the same direction and they have the point $\frac{1}{3}(a + b)$ in common so that they must lie in one straight line. In exactly the same way, with a and b interchanged, the third median will also pass through $\frac{1}{3}(a + b)$. The proof also shows, incidentally that each median is divided in the ratio 2 : 1.

1.3 The Vectors i, j, k

The dimensionality of a space can be measured by the number of mutually perpendicular vectors which can be found in it. A plane cannot have more than two perpendicular vectors and any other vector in the plane can be expressed as a linear combination of two such vectors. Similarly, in a three-dimensional space, there are three perpendicular vectors and no more. It is convenient to choose three perpendicular vectors of unit length in order to set up a coordinate system in a three-dimensional space. These are denoted by i, j, k and are a right-handed system. This is indicated in Fig. 1.4 in which i is to

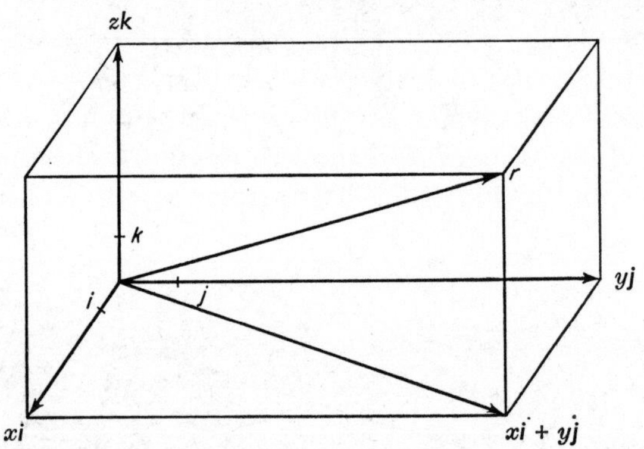

FIG. 1.4. Resolution of a vector r.

be considered as rising from the paper. Any other vector can then be expressed in terms of these three by completing the rectangular solid which has r for space diagonal and i, j, k as edges. From the definition of addition it can be seen that r is the sum of three vectors lying along these edges and of lengths x, y, z respectively so that

$$r = xi + yj + zk \tag{1.3.1}$$

The vector is said to be resolved along these axes and the numbers are its components relative to these axes. This relationship is sometimes indicated by

$$r \sim (x, y, z) \tag{1.3.2}$$

or even

$$r = (x, y, z) \tag{1.3.3}$$

but this is legitimate only if i, j, k are fixed and have been specified in relation to the problem.

When the components of two vectors are known the sum of the vectors can be found arithmetically. Thus, if

$$r = xi + yj + zk \tag{1.3.4}$$

$$s = pi + qj + rk \tag{1.3.5}$$

then the sum is

$$r + s = (x + p)i + (y + q)j + (z + r)k \tag{1.3.6}$$

The components of the vector sum are, therefore, the sum of the corresponding components of the vectors. The multiple of a vector, according to the rules, must be

$$\begin{aligned} \lambda r &= \lambda(xi + yj + zk) \\ &= \lambda xi + \lambda yj + \lambda zk \end{aligned} \tag{1.3.7}$$

and so has components multiplied by the same factor. Thus the geometrical and physical quantities represented by the vectors are easily manipulated by finding the components.

1.4 Scalar Product

The concept of multiplication can be extended to apply to vectors in three ways. Along with two vectors there can be associated, as their product, a scalar, a vector or a tensor. The scalar product can be defined as the product of the lengths of the two vectors with the cosine of the angle between them and is indicated by a dot between the vectors. The three basic vectors, for example, are of unit length and orthogonal so their scalar products are

$$\begin{aligned} i \cdot i = 1\,, \qquad i \cdot j = 0 \\ j \cdot j = 1\,, \qquad j \cdot k = 0 \\ k \cdot k = 1\,, \qquad i \cdot k = 0 \end{aligned} \tag{1.4.1}$$

Since an arbitrary multiple changes only the length of a vector the definition implies that the effect of a multiple λ is

$$a \cdot (\lambda b) = \lambda(a \cdot b) \tag{1.4.2}$$

Furthermore the order of the vectors in the product is obviously irrelevant so that

$$a \cdot b = b \cdot a \tag{1.4.3}$$

The product of the length of a vector and the cosine of the included angle gives the projected length of the vector on the other vector. Since the projected length of a sum of two vectors equals the sum of

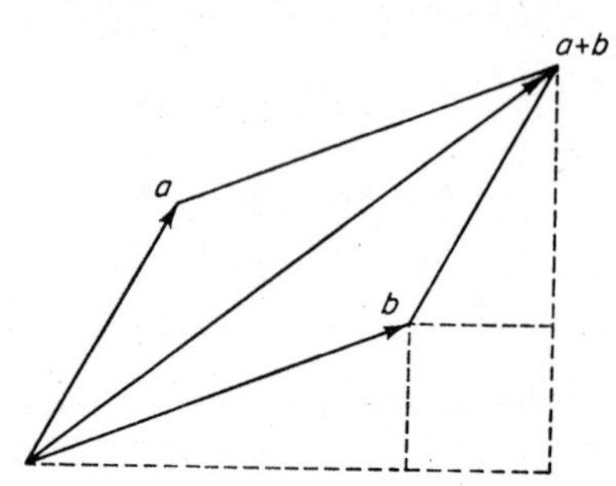

FIG. 1.5. Projection of a vector sum.

their projected lengths, as the congruent triangles in Fig. 1.5 show, it follows that the scalar product satisfies a distributive law

$$(a + b) \cdot c = a \cdot c + b \cdot c \qquad (1.4.4)$$

If the components of two vectors are known the scalar product can be calculated. Thus using (1), (2), (4) the general product can be simplified as

$$\begin{aligned} r \cdot s &= (xi + yj + zk) \cdot (pi + qj + rk) \\ &= xp + yq + zr \end{aligned} \qquad (1.4.5)$$

In particular, the length of a vector, denoted by modulus signs, is given in terms of the components by

$$|r| = \sqrt{(x^2 + y^2 + z^2)} \qquad (1.4.6)$$

and the angle θ between two vectors by

$$\cos\theta = r \cdot s/|r|\,|s| \qquad (1.4.7)$$

Orthogonal vectors in general will satisfy the equation

$$r \cdot s = 0 \qquad (1.4.8)$$

1.5 Lines and Planes

In a three-dimensional space a line can be determined by two points lying on it, or one point together with the direction of the line. Thus, if a line passes through the point a and has a direction parallel to the vector s, then the point on the line distant λs from a is, as Fig. 6 shows,

$$r = a + \lambda s \qquad (1.5.1)$$

Usually s is chosen to be a vector of unit length so that λ is the lengt along the line from a to r.

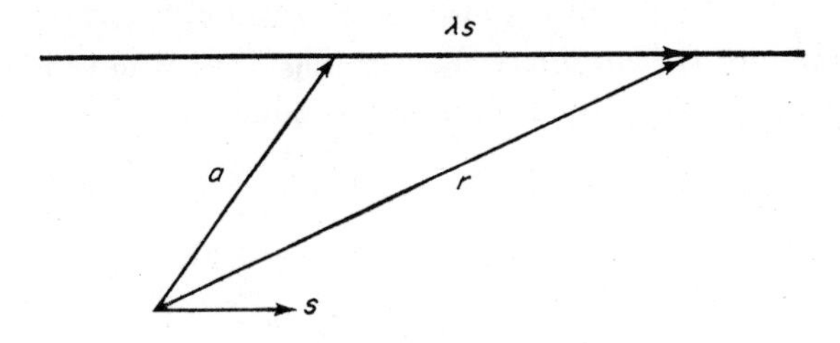

FIG. 1.6. Equation of a line.

If the components of the vectors are given by

$$r = xi + yj + zk, \qquad a = ai + bj + ck,$$
$$s = li + mj + nk \tag{1.5.2}$$

the parameter λ can be eliminated and the line is specified by the usual equations

$$\frac{x - a}{l} = \frac{y - b}{m} = \frac{z - c}{n} \tag{1.5.3}$$

Of these three equations only two are independent.

A particular plane in space can be specified in various ways but one of the simplest is to give one point on it and the direction of the normal. If this point is a and the direction is n, then any point r on the plane has the property that the line joining it to a is orthogonal to n so that

$$(r - a) \cdot n = 0 \tag{1.5.4}$$

In terms of components, with

$$n = li + mj + nk \tag{1.5.5}$$

this equation is

$$l(x - a) + m(y - b) + n(z - c) = 0 \tag{1.5.6}$$

Any linear equation will in fact represent a plane since it represents one linear restriction on the three degrees of freedom in space. Similarly it needs a pair of equations to specify a line and those in (3) do so, therefore, as the intersection of two planes.

1.6 Vector Product

For the vector product the result of multiplying two vectors is a third vector. It is a vector perpendicular to both the vectors and its magnitude is the product of the lengths of the vectors and the sine of the angle between them. The sense of the vector is such that a corkscrew rotation from the first vector to the second would produce a translation in the direction of the product. This implies that when the order of the vectors is reversed the direction of the product is also reversed

$$a \wedge b = -b \wedge a \tag{1.6.1}$$

Thus, the vector products of the basic vectors are

$$\begin{aligned} i \wedge j &= k, & j \wedge i &= -k \\ j \wedge k &= i, & k \wedge j &= -i \\ k \wedge i &= j, & i \wedge k &= -j \end{aligned} \tag{1.6.2}$$

where the symbol $\wedge$ has been used for the vector product. The vector product is also symbolized by $\times$ (cross). Because the angle is zero, the vector product of a vector with itself always vanishes

$$a \wedge a = 0 \tag{1.6.3}$$

Since the vector product is proportional to the lengths of the two vectors the vector product always satisfies

$$a \wedge (\lambda b) = \lambda (a \wedge b) \tag{1.6.4}$$

It can be proved also that the vector product satisfies the distributive law

$$a \wedge (b + c) = a \wedge b + a \wedge c \tag{1.6.5}$$

Geometrically the vector product is most easily related to areas. Its magnitude is the area of the parallelogram whose sides are the two vectors, or twice the area of the triangle also formed by them. Its direction is that of the normal to the area. It is convenient to link the area and the normal together to give a vector area and, if the vectors are edges of a solid, the sense of the vector is taken outwards.

From the rules (4), (5) the components of the vector product can be deduced. Thus

$$\begin{aligned} r \wedge s &= (xi + yj + zk) \wedge (pi + qj + rk) \\ &= (yr - zq)i + (zp - xr)j + (xq - yp)k \end{aligned} \tag{1.6.5}$$

This expression is more easily remembered in the determinantal form (see Appendix)

$$r \wedge s = \begin{vmatrix} i & j & k \\ x & y & z \\ p & q & r \end{vmatrix} \tag{1.6.6}$$

Since the vector product produces a vector, products of three or more vectors are made possible. Three vectors can be multiplied together in two different ways. The scalar triple product can be written

$$a \cdot (r \wedge s)$$

and has the value, in terms of components,

$$\begin{vmatrix} a & b & c \\ x & y & z \\ p & q & r \end{vmatrix} \tag{1.6.7}$$

The vector triple product is written as

$$a \wedge (r \wedge s)$$

and is another vector. It is evaluated in simple terms by using the identity

$$a \wedge (r \wedge s) = (a \cdot s)r - (a \cdot r)s \tag{1.6.8}$$

(see exercise 7). This identity makes clear that vector products are not associative and that brackets indicating the sequence of multiplications cannot be omitted. The vector products of larger numbers of vectors can be formed in a similar way and are reduced to simpler terms by using the same identity as often as necessary.

1.7 Applications to Solid Geometry

There are many problems of solid geometry which are difficult to solve by direct elementary methods because of the difficulties of visualization in three dimensions, but which are readily soluble using vectors.

EXAMPLE: A molecule has atoms situated at the points whose coordinates are (1, 0, 1), (2, 1, 1), (0, 1, 1). Find the bond lengths and bond angles.

By subtracting the atomic vectors in pairs, vectors parallel to the sides of the triangle are (1, 1, 0), (−1, 1, 0), (2, 0, 0) and their lengths are $\sqrt{2}$, $\sqrt{2}$, 2 respectively. From their scalar products and their lengths the bond angles are 90°, 45°, 45°.

EXAMPLE: Verify that the points (2, 0, 1), (1, 1, 2), (0, −1, 1), (−1, 0, 2) are coplanar.

If the point (2, 0, 1) is taken as a new origin the relative vectors are (−1, 1, 1), (−2, −1, 0), (−3, 0, 1). In general these three vectors will

be the sides of a parallelepiped whose volume is determined by their scalar triple product but if they are coplanar this volume will vanish.
he proof then is that

$$\begin{vmatrix} -1 & 1 & 1 \\ -2 & -1 & 0 \\ -3 & 0 & 1 \end{vmatrix} = 0$$

EXAMPLE: If the hydrostatic pressure on a face of a solid is proportional to the area of the face and is normal to the face find the pressures on the faces of the tetrahedron which has a, b, c for three adjacent edges and show that their sum vanishes.

From the definition the pressure on the face with edges a and b is proportional to $a \wedge b$. Similarly $b \wedge c$ and $c \wedge a$ give the pressures on the two adjacent faces. The fourth face has edges $a - b$, $c - b$, and so has pressure

$$(a - b) \wedge (c - b) = a \wedge c - b \wedge c - a \wedge b$$

which is just sufficient to make the total pressure over the closed surface vanish.

1.8 Bases and Reciprocal Bases

The significance of the vectors i, j, k in the theory of three dimensional vectors is that they enable any vector to be represented by three numbers, its components, and any vector operation by a corresponding operation on these numbers. Although these vectors are the ones most frequently used, any three vectors (which are not coplanar) can be used instead. A triad used in this way is called a basis. If e_1, e_2, e_3 are a basis then the arbitrary vector x is expressed in terms of these as

$$x = x^1 e_1 + x^2 e_2 + x^3 e_3 \tag{1.8.1}$$

where (x^1, x^2, x^3) are now the components of x in this basis. For reasons which will emerge later it is convenient to label these components with superscripts†. For the elementary operations of addition, subtraction and multiplication by a constant these components behave in the same way as the earlier ones.

The scalar product introduces some differences since the vectors of the basis are not necessarily orthogonal. One method of evaluating the

† x^2 should not be confused with $(x^1)^2$ nor x^3 with $(x^1)^3$.

scalar product uses the scalar products of the basis vectors defined as

$$\begin{aligned} g_{11} &= \mathbf{e}_1 \cdot \mathbf{e}_1 , & g_{12} &= \mathbf{e}_1 \cdot \mathbf{e}_2 , & g_{13} &= \mathbf{e}_1 \cdot \mathbf{e}_3 \\ g_{22} &= \mathbf{e}_2 \cdot \mathbf{e}_2 , & g_{23} &= \mathbf{e}_2 \cdot \mathbf{e}_3 , & g_{33} &= \mathbf{e}_3 \cdot \mathbf{e}_3 \end{aligned} \quad (1.8.2)$$

and the scalar product is then

$$\begin{aligned} \mathbf{x} \cdot \mathbf{y} &= (x^1\mathbf{e}_1 + x^2\mathbf{e}_2 + x^3\mathbf{e}_3) \cdot (y^1\mathbf{e}_1 + y^2\mathbf{e}_2 + y^3\mathbf{e}_3) \\ &= x^1y^1g_{11} + x^1y^2g_{12} + x^1y^3g_{13} + x^2y^1g_{21} + x^2y^2g_{22} + x^2y^3g_{23} \\ &\quad + x^3y^1g_{31} + x^3y^2g_{32} + x^3y^3g_{33} = \sum_{ij=1}^{3} x^iy^jg_{ij} \end{aligned} \quad (1.8.3)$$

The second method of evaluating the scalar product depends on introducing a second triad of vectors which is completely determined by the first and is called the reciprocal basis. These vectors are denoted by $\mathbf{e}^1$, $\mathbf{e}^2$, $\mathbf{e}^3$ and are determined by the equations

$$\begin{aligned} \mathbf{e}^1 \cdot \mathbf{e}_1 &= 1 , & \mathbf{e}^1 \cdot \mathbf{e}_2 &= 0 , & \mathbf{e}^1 \cdot \mathbf{e}_3 &= 0 \\ \mathbf{e}^2 \cdot \mathbf{e}_1 &= 0 , & \mathbf{e}^2 \cdot \mathbf{e}_2 &= 1 , & \mathbf{e}^2 \cdot \mathbf{e}_3 &= 0 \\ \mathbf{e}^3 \cdot \mathbf{e}_1 &= 0 , & \mathbf{e}^3 \cdot \mathbf{e}_2 &= 0 , & \mathbf{e}^3 \cdot \mathbf{e}_3 &= 1 \end{aligned} \quad (1.8.4)$$

Since $\mathbf{e}^1$ is perpendicular to both $\mathbf{e}_2$ and $\mathbf{e}_3$ it must lie in the direction of the vector product so that

$$\mathbf{e}^1 = \lambda \mathbf{e}_2 \wedge \mathbf{e}_3$$

and λ is fixed by the first equation which gives

$$\lambda \mathbf{e}_1 \cdot (\mathbf{e}_2 \wedge \mathbf{e}_3) = 1$$

Thus the solution of the equations is

$$\begin{aligned} \mathbf{e}^1 &= \mathbf{e}_2 \wedge \mathbf{e}_3/\mathbf{e}_1 \cdot (\mathbf{e}_2 \wedge \mathbf{e}_3) \\ \mathbf{e}^2 &= \mathbf{e}_3 \wedge \mathbf{e}_1/\mathbf{e}_1 \cdot (\mathbf{e}_2 \wedge \mathbf{e}_3) \\ \mathbf{e}^3 &= \mathbf{e}_1 \wedge \mathbf{e}_2/\mathbf{e}_1 \cdot (\mathbf{e}_2 \wedge \mathbf{e}_3) \end{aligned} \quad (1.8.5)$$

When these vectors are used as basis vectors the components of $\mathbf{x}$ are denoted by (x_1, x_2, x_3) and

$$\mathbf{x} = x_1\mathbf{e}^1 + x_2\mathbf{e}^2 + x_3\mathbf{e}^3 \quad (1.8.6)$$

The scalar product of two vectors can now be evaluated easily if one vector is referred to the original basis and the other to the reciprocal basis

$$\begin{aligned} \mathbf{x} \cdot \mathbf{y} &= (x^1\mathbf{e}_1 + x^2\mathbf{e}_2 + x^3\mathbf{e}_3) \cdot (y_1\mathbf{e}^1 + y_2\mathbf{e}^2 + y_3\mathbf{e}^3) \\ &= x^1y_1 + x^2y_2 + x^3y_3 \end{aligned} \quad (1.8.7)$$

Each vector in space has therefore two sets of components. The first set (x^1, x^2, x^3) are called contravariant and the second, (x_1, x_2, x_3), covariant. The distinguishing feature of $\mathbf{i}, \mathbf{j}, \mathbf{k}$ as a basis is that they are their own reciprocals. Components relative to $\mathbf{i}, \mathbf{j}, \mathbf{k}$ are then both contravariant and covariant.

The practical value of these more general bases can be seen, for example, in crystallography. The unit cell of the crystal provides a natural starting point and three adjacent edges can be taken as basis vectors. The position of a nucleus in the cell is then specified by the contravariant components (a^1, a^2, a^3) so that all the corresponding nuclei in other unit cells have the components

$$(a^1 + l\,, a^2 + m\,, a^3 + n) \tag{1.8.8}$$

where l, m, n are positive or negative integers. On the other hand, a plane satisfies an equation of the form

$$\mathbf{k} \cdot \mathbf{r} = p \tag{1.8.9}$$

and the normal, $\mathbf{k}$, is most conveniently specified by its covariant components in order that the scalar product may remain simple. In particular, a lattice plane may be defined as a plane passing through at least three non-linear lattice points, i.e. corners of cells. These lattice planes can be grouped into sets which are all parallel to one another and have a constant spacing. The plane of the set which passes closest to the origin has the equation

$$\sum_i k_i x^i = 1 \tag{1.8.10}$$

where the components k_i are integers. The other parallel planes are then

$$\sum_i k_i x^i = n \tag{1.8.11}$$

where n is an integer, so that the spacing is

$$|\mathbf{k}|^{-1}$$

The vector $\mathbf{k}$ thus specifies both the direction of the normal to the planes and the spacing and so fixes the set. Since the k_i are integers all the possible $\mathbf{k}$ lie on a lattice, known as the reciprocal lattice, with $\mathbf{e}^1$, $\mathbf{e}^2$, $\mathbf{e}^3$ as the edges of its unit cell.

1.9 Transformations of Bases

The relations between a vector and its contravariant and covariant components become clearer when the consequences are considered of a change from one basis to another. The vectors of the new basis $\bar{\mathbf{e}}_1$, $\bar{\mathbf{e}}_2$, $\bar{\mathbf{e}}_3$ have components relative to the old basis so that

$$\begin{aligned} \bar{\mathbf{e}}_1 &= t_1^1\mathbf{e}_1 + t_1^2\mathbf{e}_2 + t_1^3\mathbf{e}_3 \\ \bar{\mathbf{e}}_2 &= t_2^1\mathbf{e}_1 + t_2^2\mathbf{e}_2 + t_2^3\mathbf{e}_3 \\ \bar{\mathbf{e}}_3 &= t_3^1\mathbf{e}_1 + t_3^2\mathbf{e}_2 + t_3^3\mathbf{e}_3 \end{aligned} \tag{1.9.1}$$

Now if x is an arbitrary vector, its components relative to the two bases can be defined by

$$\mathsf{x} = x^1\mathbf{e}_1 + x^2\mathbf{e}_2 + x^3\mathbf{e}_3 = \bar{x}^1\bar{\mathbf{e}}_1 + \bar{x}^2\bar{\mathbf{e}}_2 + \bar{x}^3\bar{\mathbf{e}}_3 \tag{1.9.2}$$

and, if the equations for the $\bar{\mathbf{e}}_1$ are substituted into these, they satisfy

$$\begin{aligned} x^1 &= t_1^1\bar{x}^1 + t_2^1\bar{x}^2 + t_3^1\bar{x}^3 \\ x^2 &= t_1^2\bar{x}^1 + t_2^2\bar{x}^2 + t_3^2\bar{x}^3 \\ x^3 &= t_1^3\bar{x}^1 + t_2^3\bar{x}^2 + t_3^3\bar{x}^3 \end{aligned} \tag{1.9.3}$$

These equations can be solved for the new components giving

$$\begin{aligned} \bar{x}^1 &= T_1^1x^1 + T_2^1x^2 + T_3^1x^3 \\ \bar{x}^2 &= T_1^2x^1 + T_2^2x^2 + T_3^2x^3 \\ \bar{x}^3 &= T_1^3x^1 + T_2^3x^2 + T_3^3x^3 \end{aligned} \tag{1.9.4}$$

where the coefficients T_i^j are related to the previous coefficients t_i^j by the nine equations

$$\begin{aligned} \sum_j T_j^i t_i^j &= 1\,, \qquad \text{all } i \\ \sum_j T_j^i t_k^j &= 0\,, \qquad \text{all } i \neq k \end{aligned} \tag{1.9.5}$$

These equations can be combined into a more convenient form by defining the Kronecker delta

$$\delta_k^i = \begin{cases} 1, & \text{if } i = k \\ 0, & \text{if } i \neq k \end{cases} \tag{1.9.6}$$

so that

$$\sum_j T_j^i t_k^j = \delta_k^i \tag{1.9.7}$$

Practical methods of solving these equations are discussed in 3.3

The reciprocal bases are also related for, if the new triad $\bar{\mathbf{e}}^i$ is expressed in terms of the old $\mathbf{e}^k$ by

$$\bar{\mathbf{e}}^i = \sum_k S_k^i \mathbf{e}^k \tag{1.9.8}$$

then since, by definition,

$$\bar{\mathrm{e}}^i \cdot \bar{\mathrm{e}}_j = \delta^i_j$$

$$\left(\sum_k S^i_k \mathrm{e}^k\right) \cdot \left(\sum_l t^l_j \mathrm{e}_l\right) = \delta^i_j$$

$$\sum_k S^i_k t^k_j = \delta^i_j$$

so that

$$S^i_k = T^i_k \tag{1.9.9}$$

In a similar way the covariant components of a vector satisfy

$$\bar{x}_i = \sum_j t^j_i x_j \tag{1.9.10}$$

Thus the two sets of coefficients t^j_i, T^j_i are sufficient to relate corresponding quantities in the two bases. The term covariant is applied to these components because they transform in the same way as the original basis whereas the contravariant components transform with the reciprocal transformation.

The metrical constants g_{ik} are also changed by the transformation to $\bar{g}_{lm}$ with

$$\bar{g}_{lm} = \bar{\mathrm{e}}_l \cdot \bar{\mathrm{e}}_m \tag{1.9.11}$$

The relation is more elaborate since

$$\bar{\mathrm{e}}_l \cdot \bar{\mathrm{e}}_m = \left(\sum_i t^i_l \mathrm{e}_i\right) \cdot \left(\sum_k t^k_m \mathrm{e}_k\right)$$

and so

$$\bar{g}_{lm} = \sum_{ik} t^i_l t^k_m g_{ik} \tag{1.9.12}$$

1.10 *n*-dimensional Vectors

The theory of 3-dimensional vectors can be generalized to include vectors in an n-dimensional vector space with only a few changes. To span the space the basis must contain n vectors

$$\mathrm{e}_1, \quad \mathrm{e}_2, \quad \ldots, \quad \mathrm{e}_n$$

An arbitrary vector x will have n components x^i such that

$$\mathrm{x} = x^1\mathrm{e}_1 + x^2\mathrm{e}_2 + \ldots + x^n\mathrm{e}_n \tag{1.10.1}$$

Addition of two vectors is equivalent to addition of their components

$$\mathrm{x} + \mathrm{y} = \sum_i (x^i + y^i)\mathrm{e}_i \tag{1.10.2}$$

and similarly for multiplication by a scalar

$$\lambda\mathrm{x} = \sum_i (\lambda x^i)\mathrm{e}_i \tag{1.10.3}$$

The usual distributive laws hold.

The scalar product of two vectors can be calculated from the components in two ways. If the contravariant components alone are known the formula involves the double summation

$$\mathsf{x} \cdot \mathsf{y} = \sum_{l,m} x^l y^m g_{lm} \tag{1.10.4}$$

but if both components are known the single summation relations

$$\mathsf{x} \cdot \mathsf{y} = \sum_i x_i y^i = \sum_i x^i y_i \tag{1.10.5}$$

are simpler. The metric constants g_{ik} are defined by

$$g_{ik} = \mathbf{e}_i \cdot \mathbf{e}_k \tag{1.10.6}$$

The reciprocal basis $\mathbf{e}^i$ is defined, as before, by the equations

$$\mathbf{e}^i \cdot \mathbf{e}_k = \delta^i_k \tag{1.10.7}$$

and the covariant components of x satisfy

$$\mathsf{x} = \sum_i x_i \mathbf{e}^i \tag{1.10.8}$$

The transformation of these components, as the basis is transformed to a new basis, gives equations which generalize the 3-dimensional equations above. Thus, if the new basis vectors $\bar{\mathbf{e}}_i$ are defined by the equations

$$\bar{\mathbf{e}}_i = \sum_k t^k_i \mathbf{e}_k , \qquad i = 1, \ldots, n \tag{1.10.9}$$

then the covariant components $\bar{x}_i$ of an arbitrary vector x in the new basis system satisfy

$$\bar{x}_i = \sum_k t^k_i x_k , \qquad i = 1, \ldots, n \tag{1.10.10}$$

The contravariant components will then satisfy

$$\bar{x}^i = \sum_k T^i_k x^k , \qquad i = 1, \ldots, n \tag{1.10.11}$$

where

$$\sum_j T^i_j t^j_k = \delta^i_k , \qquad i, k = 1, \ldots, n \tag{1.10.12}$$

It is a considerable advantage in handling equations such as these if conventions are adopted about indices which enable redundant symbols to be omitted. The first convention which will now be adopted is that in any equation an index which appears once on each side of the equation (a "free" index) will be assumed to take on, in turn, all values from

1 to n depending on the dimension of the space. The second convention is that an index which is repeated on one side of an equation will always imply a sum of all such terms even though the summation sign is omitted. This repeated index always occurs once as a contravariant index and once as a covariant index. The sum implied is over all values of the index so that the particular letter used to denote the sum is irrelevant and can be changed at will (a "dummy" index). Thus, for example, the equations (12) can be written as

$$T^i_j t^j_k = \delta^i_k \tag{1.10.13}$$

and the dimension n is fixed once for all by the context of a particular application and need not enter the general equation.

1.11 Generalized Rotation of Basis

Among all the transformations of bases considered above there is one class which has particular importance. It may be distinguished by the property that all its transformations leave the basis vectors with the same relative properties. These relative properties are summed up in the g_{ik} matrix which is therefore left invariant. Thus the transformations satisfy the equations

$$g_{ik} = t^l_i t^m_k g_{lm} \tag{1.11.1}$$

If the basis vectors are orthogonal and of unit length (i.e. orthonormal) then this restriction ensures that the transformed basis is also orthonormal and the transformation is a pure rotation with

$$\delta_{ik} = \sum_l t^l_i t^l_k \tag{1.11.2}$$

For this reason transformations satisfying (1) may be called generalized rotations.

Since, in an orthonormal basis, there is no distinction between covariant and contravariant components the equations above imply the simple relation

$$T^i_l = t^l_i \tag{1.11.3}$$

This relation also ensures that components of any tensor transform in the same way irrespective of whether they are written as covariant or contravariant.

In the special theory of relativity it is often convenient to choose a basis system such that

$$g_{11} = g_{22} = g_{33} = 1, \quad g_{44} = -1 \quad \text{and} \quad g_{ik} = 0 \quad \text{for} \quad i \neq k$$

The corresponding generalized rotations are the Lorentz transformations.

1.12 Applications to Molecules

A molecule having N atoms has $3N$ degrees of freedom. The configuration of the molecule can then be specified by the components of a vector in a $3N$-dimensional space. One set of basis vectors for this space consists of configurations in which one atom is displaced along a unit vector parallel to one of the three unit vectors of the space and the other atoms remain in their equilibrium positions. The components of a displacement relative to this basis will consist of the components of the N 3-dimensional vectors which specify the displacements of the N nuclei from their equilibrium positions.

This choice of basis is not usually the most convenient one to describe the motion of the nuclei and transformations have to be made to other bases. It is desirable, for example, that the translational and rotational motions should be distinguished from the vibrational. This can be done by first giving the components corresponding to pure translation and pure rotation of the system. Then an arbitrary displacement is taken and modified so that there is no linear or angular momentum involved. This can be repeated $(3N - 6)$ times to give independent displacements of the system. This procedure is equivalent to introducing a new set of basis vectors

$$\bar{\mathbf{e}}_i = t_i^j \mathbf{e}_j \tag{1.12.1}$$

where t_i^j gives the components of the pure translation, pure rotation and the remaining $(3N - 6)$ displacements relative to the original basis. The components of an arbitrary displacement in the two bases are connected by

$$x^i = t_j^i \bar{x}^j \tag{1.12.2}$$

and this enables the equations of motion given in terms of the original vector components to be transformed into terms of components relative to the new basis. The basis vectors $\bar{\mathbf{e}}_i$ give the easiest way of picturing the transformation and the t_i^j can be easily read off.

It is often convenient to insist that this transformation should be a rotation since this enables the kinetic energy to be expressed more simply. It also enables the inverse transformation to be found immediately and

$$\begin{aligned} \bar{x}^i &= T_j^i x^j \\ &= \sum_j t_i^j x^j \end{aligned} \tag{1.12.3}$$

This equation is then very similar in form to the equation for $\bar{\mathbf{e}}_i$ since the summations are over the same coefficients.

APPENDIX

Determinants

The principal properties of determinants used in this and later chapters are summarized here for convenience.

A determinant is a number obtained by combining together the numbers which are written as elements in a square array. The operation of combining them is denoted by vertical lines. The number of rows and columns in the array is called the order. A second order determinant, for example, is defined as

$$\begin{vmatrix} a & b \\ c & d \end{vmatrix} = ad - bc$$

For higher order determinants the element in the ith row and the jth column is denoted by subscripts, e.g. a_{ij} and the determinant is defined as

$$|a_{ij}| = \begin{vmatrix} a_{11} & a_{12} & a_{13} \dots a_{1n} \\ a_{21} & a_{22} & \dots & \\ \vdots & & & \\ a_{n1} & \dots & & a_{nn} \end{vmatrix}$$

$$= \sum_P (-)^P P a_{11} a_{22} \dots a_{nn}$$

where P is a permutation of the column indices in the product and the sum includes all these permutations with a negative sign if the permutation is odd, i.e. expressible as the product of an odd number of interchanges.

The cofactor A_{ij} of any element a_{ij} in a determinant is a determinant formed by omitting the entire ith row and jth column from the original determinant and prefixing the sign $(-)^{i+j}$. The determinant can be expressed as the sum of the elements in any one row or column each multiplied by its cofactor e.g.

$$|a_{ij}| = \sum_i a_{ij} A_{ij} \qquad \text{any } j$$

$$= \sum_j a_{ij} A_{ij} \qquad \text{any } i$$

By repeating this expansion a determinant can be expressed in terms of determinants of steadily smaller order and hence evaluated.

Whenever two rows (or two columns) of a determinant are interchanged the value of the determinant is changed only in its sign. It follows from this that if two rows (or columns) are identical the determinant vanishes. When one row (or column) is multiplied by a constant the value of the determinant is multiplied by the same constant.

EXERCISES

1. Prove that the perpendiculars from the vertices of a triangle are concurrent.
2. Prove that the lines from the vertices of a tetrahedron to the centroids of opposite faces are concurrent.
3. Show that the parametric equation of the line joining a and b is

$$r = (1-\lambda)\, a + \lambda b$$

4. Show that the plane through a, b, c can be represented parametrically as

$$r = (1 - \lambda - \mu)\, a + \lambda b + \mu c$$

5. The points a, b, c, d are coplanar when

$$a.[c \wedge (d - b)] = d.[b \wedge (c - a)]$$

6. The vectors $a + 2b + c$, $a + b - 2c$ and $a + 3b + 4c$ lie in a plane through the origin.
7. Prove that $a \wedge (r \wedge s) = (a \,.\, s)r - (a \,.\, r)s$ by evaluating the components of both sides.
8. Show that the equation of the plane through r_1, r_2, r_3 is

$$\begin{vmatrix} x & y & z & 1 \\ x_1 & y_1 & z_1 & 1 \\ x_2 & y_2 & z_2 & 1 \\ x_3 & y_3 & z_3 & 1 \end{vmatrix} = 0$$

9. Show that the lines $r = a + \lambda u$; $r = b + \mu v$ intersect if $a \,.\, (u \wedge v) = b \,.\, (u \wedge v)$.
10. Verify that, in general

$$(a \wedge b) \wedge (c \wedge d) \neq a \wedge (b \wedge [c \wedge d])$$

11. Show that $(a - b) \,.\, (u \wedge v)/|u \wedge v|$ is the shortest distance between the non-intersecting lines $r = a + \lambda u$, $r = b + \mu v$.
12. By dividing into tetrahedra, or using vectors, prove that the total hydrostatic pressure over all the faces of a parallelepiped vanishes.
13. Prove that the reciprocal vectors to the reciprocal vectors are the basis vectors.
14. A 2-dimensional lattice is generated by a vector of length 2 and a second of unit length at 60° to it. Sketch the lines whose k_i are (1, 0) and (4, 1) and show that they are orthogonal and similarly for (0, 1) and (1, 1).
15. Find three orthogonal vectors sufficient to describe the vibrations of an X_2Y molecule.

CHAPTER 2

MATRICES

2.1 Introduction

In chapter 1, as well as the vector components which were labelled with one index, quantities labelled with two indices, such as the transformation t_j^k and the metrical constants g_{ik}, have been introduced. This chapter is concerned with the rules for manipulating such quantities and for dividing them into various categories. The meaning of these quantities themselves will be discussed in a later chapter and it is sufficient at present to note that they act on a vector to produce another vector.

Throughout chapters 2, 3, 4 the basis vectors $\mathbf{e}_i$ will be taken as fixed and orthonormal. The vectors themselves will not be used but only their components. The orthonormality of the basis means that the distinction between covariant and contravariant components disappears and it is possible to write all indices as subscripts. It is convenient now to introduce a single symbol $\boldsymbol{a}$ to refer to all the components a_i together. In general, these components will be written in a column, i.e.

$$\boldsymbol{a} = \begin{pmatrix} a_1 \\ a_2 \\ \vdots \\ a_n \end{pmatrix} \tag{2.1.1}$$

Any quantity depending on two indices will be called a matrix. Its components are known as elements and are written as a rectangular array. The two indices label the rows and columns of this array. A matrix with m rows and n columns is said to be of order $m \times n$. Thus the matrix g_{ik} has order $n \times n$ and is written as †

† The use of brackets, either round or square, distinguishes a matrix from a determinant.

$$g_{ik} = \begin{pmatrix} g_{11} & g_{12} & g_{13} \dots g_{1n} \\ g_{21} & g_{22} & \dots \\ \vdots & & \\ g_{n1} & & & g_{nn} \end{pmatrix} \tag{2.1.2}$$

For the matrix t_i^k there is a choice of which index refers to the row. The ambiguity is resolved when the indices are spaced appropriately so that

$$t_i{}^k = \begin{pmatrix} t_1{}^1 & t_1{}^2 & t_1{}^3 \\ t_2{}^1 & t_2{}^2 & t_2{}^3 \\ t_3{}^1 & t_3{}^2 & t_3{}^3 \end{pmatrix} \tag{2.1.3}$$

while

$$t^k{}_i = \begin{pmatrix} t^1{}_1 & t^1{}_2 & t^1{}_3 \\ t^2{}_1 & t^2{}_2 & t^2{}_3 \\ t^3{}_1 & t^3{}_2 & t^3{}_3 \end{pmatrix} \tag{2.1.4}$$

To symbolize these matrix arrays, it is convenient to use bold upper case letters so that in various circumstances three notations will be used

$$\boldsymbol{A} = a_{in} = \begin{pmatrix} a_{11} & a_{12} \dots a_{1n} \\ a_{21} & \\ \vdots & \\ a_{m1} & \dots & a_{mn} \end{pmatrix} \tag{2.1.5}$$

This more abstract notation enables the resemblances between the manipulation of matrices and of vector components to be emphasized since the column vector behaves like an $n \times 1$ order matrix.

2.2 Matrix Arithmetic

Just as the sum of two vectors is found by adding their components each to each, so two matrices are added by adding corresponding elements. Thus the sum of the matrix a_{ik} and the matrix b_{ik} is a matrix with elements

$$a_{ik} + b_{ik}$$

or, in more detail,

$$\begin{pmatrix} a_{11} & a_{12} & a_{13} \dots a_{1n} \\ a_{21} & & \\ & & \\ a_{m1} & \dots & a_{mn} \end{pmatrix} + \begin{pmatrix} b_{11} & b_{12} & b_{13} \dots b_{1n} \\ b_{21} & & \\ \vdots & & \\ b_{m1} & \dots & b_{mn} \end{pmatrix} =$$

$$= \begin{pmatrix} a_{11} + b_{11} & a_{12} + b_{12} & a_{13} + b_{13} \dots & a_{1n} + b_{1n} \\ a_{21} + b_{21} & & & \\ \vdots & & & \\ a_{m1} + b_{m1} & \dots & & a_{mn} + b_{mn} \end{pmatrix} \tag{2.2.1}$$

Not only is this the most natural definition but it is the one that ensures consistent results when matrices act on vectors to produce vectors. If

$$x_i = a_{ik}z_k, \qquad y_i = b_{ik}z_k \tag{2.2.2}$$

then

$$x_i + y_i = (a_{ik} + b_{ik})z_k \tag{2.2.3}$$

so that the sum of the vectors is found from z by using the sum of the matrices. This definition of addition is valid only when the two matrices have the same order.

Another elementary operation is the multiplication of a matrix by a constant. This is done by multiplying every element by the constant. This definition is consistent with the definition of addition for, when $b_{ik} = a_{ik}$,

$$a_{ik} + a_{ik} = 2a_{ik} \tag{2.2.4}$$

The constant may also be a negative number and consequently means that matrices can be subtracted by subtracting their components. If λ and μ are constants then the distributive laws hold

$$(\lambda + \mu)a_{ik} = \lambda a_{ik} + \mu a_{ik} \tag{2.2.5}$$

$$\lambda(a_{ik} + b_{ik}) = \lambda a_{ik} + \lambda b_{ik} \tag{2.2.6}$$

Matrix equations such as (6) are subject to the same convention about free indices as vector equations and so imply mn separate equations for each matrix element. This is perhaps more obvious in the abstract notation for (6), viz.

$$\lambda(\boldsymbol{A} + \boldsymbol{B}) = \lambda\boldsymbol{A} + \lambda\boldsymbol{B}\,. \tag{2.2.7}$$

Another instance of this is the obvious equation

$$a_{ik} - a_{ik} = 0 \tag{2.2.8}$$

and, in order to write this symbolically, a null matrix $\boldsymbol{O}$ all of whose elements are zero is needed so that (8) becomes

$$\boldsymbol{A} - \boldsymbol{A} = \boldsymbol{O} \tag{2.2.9}$$

The effect of these rules is that matrices behave, on addition and multiplication by constants, just as vectors with mn components except that these components are written in an array instead of a column. To exploit this connection further it is useful to introduce the basic matrices $\boldsymbol{E}_{ij}$ all of whose components vanish except for the one labelled ij, which is unity. The subscripts on this symbol do not refer, it must be emphasized, to the elements of the matrix but to all the different matrices. The arbitrary matrix $\boldsymbol{A}$ can then be expressed as the double sum

$$\boldsymbol{A} = a_{ik}\boldsymbol{E}_{ik} \tag{2.2.10}$$

in analogy with the expression (1.10.1) for vectors.

2.3 Multiplication

Two matrices can act in succession on a vector to produce a new vector. Thus if the original vector is $\boldsymbol{x}$ the effect of the first matrix is to give a vector $\boldsymbol{y}$ with

$$y_i = a_{ik}x_k \tag{2.3.1}$$

The second matrix acts on $\boldsymbol{y}$ to give the final vector $\boldsymbol{z}$ with

$$z_i = b_{ik}y_k \tag{2.3.2}$$

and since

$$z_i = b_{ik}a_{kl}x_l \tag{2.3.3}$$

the combined effect is equivalent to a matrix

$$c_{il} = b_{ik}a_{kl} \tag{2.3.4}$$

This combination of the two matrices is known as their product. In symbolic notation the product will be indicated by the juxtaposition of the two matrices, i.e. (4) becomes

$$\boldsymbol{C} = \boldsymbol{BA} \tag{2.3.5}$$

In order to form the product the number of columns of the first matrix must equal the number of rows of the second but there is no other restriction on the order. Thus the action of a matrix on a vector is also a product of the same type so that (1) becomes

$$\boldsymbol{y} = \boldsymbol{Ax} \tag{2.3.6}$$

It follows from the definition that matrix multiplication satisfies the laws

$$\boldsymbol{A}(\boldsymbol{BC}) = (\boldsymbol{AB})\boldsymbol{C} \tag{2.3.7}$$

$$\boldsymbol{A}(\boldsymbol{B}+\boldsymbol{C}) = \boldsymbol{AB}+\boldsymbol{AC} \tag{2.3.8}$$

$$(\lambda\boldsymbol{A})\boldsymbol{B} = \lambda(\boldsymbol{AB}) \tag{2.3.9}$$

The Kronecker delta matrix has special significance in relation to matrix multiplication for

$$a_{ik}\delta_{kl} = a_{il} = \delta_{ik}a_{kl} \tag{2.3.10}$$

It will be denoted by the symbol $\boldsymbol{I}$ so that (10) becomes

$$\boldsymbol{AI} = \boldsymbol{A} = \boldsymbol{IA} \tag{2.3.11}$$

In practical terms the matrix product implies the accumulated sums of products of numbers one from a row and one from a column. A sum of this type can be calculated in one operation on a calculating machine and so is a convenient unit of calculation. The simplest example is the scalar product of two vectors. In order that a column of numbers may be turned into a row of numbers an operation known as transposing is needed and it will be denoted by a tilde. Thus if

$$\boldsymbol{x} = \begin{pmatrix} x_1 \\ x_2 \\ \vdots \\ x_n \end{pmatrix} \tag{2.3.12}$$

then its transpose is

$$\tilde{\boldsymbol{x}} = (x_1 x_2 \ldots x_n) \tag{2.3.13}$$

The scalar product can then be written as

$$\tilde{\boldsymbol{x}}\boldsymbol{y} = (x_1 x_2 \,..\, x_n)\begin{pmatrix} y_1 \\ y_2 \\ \vdots \\ y_n \end{pmatrix} = x_i y_i \tag{2.3.14}$$

If the matrix $\boldsymbol{A}$ is written as a column of row vectors

$$\boldsymbol{A} = \begin{pmatrix} \boldsymbol{a}_{1\cdot} \\ \boldsymbol{a}_{2\cdot} \\ \vdots \\ \boldsymbol{a}_{m\cdot} \end{pmatrix} \tag{2.3.15}$$

where the symbol $\boldsymbol{a}_{i\cdot}$ is defined as the vector of the ith row

$$\boldsymbol{a}_{i\cdot} = (a_{i1}a_{i2} \ldots a_{in}) \tag{2.3.16}$$

then its product with a vector can be written

$$\boldsymbol{Ax} = \begin{pmatrix} \boldsymbol{a}_{1\cdot}\ \boldsymbol{x} \\ \boldsymbol{a}_{2\cdot}\ \boldsymbol{x} \\ \vdots \\ \boldsymbol{a}_{m\cdot}\ \boldsymbol{x} \end{pmatrix} \tag{2.3.17}$$

and this emphasizes the fact that the product is merely a succession of scalar products. A matrix can also be regarded as a row of column vectors, e.g.

$$\boldsymbol{B} = (\boldsymbol{b}_{\cdot 1}\ \boldsymbol{b}_{\cdot 2}\ \boldsymbol{b}_{\cdot 3} \ldots \boldsymbol{b}_{\cdot p}) \tag{2.3.18}$$

where the column vector is

$$\boldsymbol{b}_{\cdot i} = \begin{pmatrix} b_{1i} \\ b_{2i} \\ \vdots \\ b_{ni} \end{pmatrix} \tag{2.3.19}$$

This enables the product of two matrices to be treated as a number of scalar products for each element in the product matrix is a scalar product and

$$\boldsymbol{AB} = \begin{pmatrix} \boldsymbol{a}_{1\cdot} \\ \boldsymbol{a}_{2\cdot} \\ \vdots \\ \boldsymbol{a}_{m\cdot} \end{pmatrix} (\boldsymbol{b}_{\cdot 1}\quad \boldsymbol{b}_{\cdot 2}\quad \ldots\quad \boldsymbol{b}_{\cdot p}) \tag{2.3.20}$$

$$= \begin{pmatrix} \boldsymbol{a}_{1\cdot}.\boldsymbol{b}_{\cdot 1} & \boldsymbol{a}_{1\cdot}.\boldsymbol{b}_{\cdot 2} & \ldots & \boldsymbol{a}_{1\cdot}.\boldsymbol{b}_{\cdot p} \\ \boldsymbol{a}_{2\cdot}.\boldsymbol{b}_{\cdot 1} & & & \\ \vdots & & & \\ \boldsymbol{a}_{m\cdot}.\boldsymbol{b}_{\cdot 1} & & & \boldsymbol{a}_{m\cdot}.\boldsymbol{b}_{\cdot p} \end{pmatrix} \tag{2.3.21}$$

Matrix multiplication differs from most other forms of multiplication in one essential respect, namely that it is not commutative. In general, the product of two matrices is entirely different when the order is reversed. This is the feature which enables quantum mechanical operators to be represented by matrices since the commutation rules of the operators can be matched by the commutation rules of the matrices. The spin operators S_x, S_y, S_z, for example, satisfy the relations

$$\begin{aligned} \mathsf{S}_x\mathsf{S}_y - \mathsf{S}_y\mathsf{S}_x &= i\mathsf{S}_z \\ \mathsf{S}_y\mathsf{S}_z - \mathsf{S}_z\mathsf{S}_y &= i\mathsf{S}_x \\ \mathsf{S}_z\mathsf{S}_x - \mathsf{S}_x\mathsf{S}_z &= i\mathsf{S}_y \end{aligned} \tag{2.3.22}$$

and so cannot be represented by ordinary numbers. They can be represented, however, by the matrices

$$\mathsf{S}_x \sim \tfrac{1}{2}\begin{pmatrix} 0 & 1 \\ 1 & 0 \end{pmatrix}, \quad \mathsf{S}_y \sim \tfrac{1}{2}\begin{pmatrix} 0 & -i \\ i & 0 \end{pmatrix}, \quad \mathsf{S}_z \sim \tfrac{1}{2}\begin{pmatrix} 1 & 0 \\ 0 & -1 \end{pmatrix} \tag{2.3.23}$$

since these satisfy the same equations.

In some applications permutation matrices are important. A permutation matrix is obtained by applying a permutation to the row vectors of $\boldsymbol{I}$. The effect of pre-multiplying a matrix by a permutation matrix is to apply the same permutation to its rows, e.g.

$$\begin{pmatrix} 0 & 1 & 0 & 0 \\ 0 & 0 & 1 & 0 \\ 1 & 0 & 0 & 0 \\ 0 & 0 & 0 & 1 \end{pmatrix}\begin{pmatrix} a_{11} & a_{12} & a_{13} & a_{14} \\ a_{21} & a_{22} & a_{23} & a_{24} \\ a_{31} & a_{32} & a_{33} & a_{34} \\ a_{41} & a_{42} & a_{43} & a_{44} \end{pmatrix} = \begin{pmatrix} a_{21} & a_{22} & a_{23} & a_{24} \\ a_{31} & a_{32} & a_{33} & a_{34} \\ a_{11} & a_{12} & a_{13} & a_{14} \\ a_{41} & a_{42} & a_{43} & a_{44} \end{pmatrix} \tag{2.3.24}$$

while post-multiplication applies the inverse permutation to its columns e.g.

$$\begin{pmatrix} a_{11} & a_{12} & a_{13} & a_{14} \\ a_{21} & a_{22} & a_{23} & a_{24} \\ a_{31} & a_{32} & a_{33} & a_{34} \\ a_{41} & a_{42} & a_{43} & a_{44} \end{pmatrix}\begin{pmatrix} 0 & 1 & 0 & 0 \\ 0 & 0 & 1 & 0 \\ 1 & 0 & 0 & 0 \\ 0 & 0 & 0 & 1 \end{pmatrix} = \begin{pmatrix} a_{13} & a_{11} & a_{12} & a_{14} \\ a_{23} & a_{21} & a_{22} & a_{24} \\ a_{33} & a_{31} & a_{32} & a_{34} \\ a_{43} & a_{41} & a_{42} & a_{44} \end{pmatrix} \tag{2.3.25}$$

The effect of pre- and post-multiplication by the basis matrices $\boldsymbol{E}_{ij}$ is also interesting. Pre-multiplication by $\boldsymbol{E}_{ij}$ gives a matrix of zero elements except for the ith row which contains the elements of the original jth row, e.g.

$$\boldsymbol{E}_{12}\boldsymbol{A} = \begin{pmatrix} 0 & 1 & 0 & 0 \\ 0 & 0 & 0 & 0 \\ 0 & 0 & 0 & 0 \\ 0 & 0 & 0 & 0 \end{pmatrix}\begin{pmatrix} a_{11} & a_{12} & a_{13} & a_{14} \\ a_{21} & a_{22} & a_{23} & a_{24} \\ a_{31} & a_{32} & a_{33} & a_{34} \\ a_{41} & a_{42} & a_{43} & a_{44} \end{pmatrix} = \begin{pmatrix} a_{21} & a_{22} & a_{23} & a_{24} \\ 0 & 0 & 0 & 0 \\ 0 & 0 & 0 & 0 \\ 0 & 0 & 0 & 0 \end{pmatrix} \tag{2.3.26}$$

or

$$\boldsymbol{E}_{12}\begin{pmatrix} \boldsymbol{a}_{1\cdot} \\ \boldsymbol{a}_{2\cdot} \\ \boldsymbol{a}_{3\cdot} \\ \boldsymbol{a}_{4\cdot} \end{pmatrix} = \begin{pmatrix} \boldsymbol{a}_{2\cdot} \\ 0 \\ 0 \\ 0 \end{pmatrix} \tag{2.3.27}$$

Post-multiplication by $\boldsymbol{E}_{ij}$ also gives a zero matrix except for the jth column which contains the original ith column, e.g.

$$(\boldsymbol{a}_{\cdot 1}\ \boldsymbol{a}_{\cdot 2}\ \boldsymbol{a}_{\cdot 3}\ \boldsymbol{a}_{\cdot 4})\boldsymbol{E}_{12} = (0\ \boldsymbol{a}_{\cdot 1}\ 0\ 0) \tag{2.3.28}$$

These basis matrices may be used, therefore, to extract rows or columns from a matrix. By combining pre- and post-multiplication single elements can be extracted. Thus the product

$$\boldsymbol{E}_{ij}\boldsymbol{A}\boldsymbol{E}_{lm}$$

gives a matrix of zeroes except for the imth element which is a_{jl}.

2.4 Associated Matrices

With every matrix there is associated a number of matrices derived from it by simple operations. These operations are now given names and symbols.

The first operation is that of taking the complex conjugate of each element and will be denoted by a star so that

$$\boldsymbol{A}^* = a_{ik}^* = \begin{pmatrix} a_{11}^* & a_{12}^* & \dots & a_{1n}^* \\ \dots & & & \\ a_{m1}^* & & \dots & a_{mn}^* \end{pmatrix} \tag{2.4.1}$$

The second operation is transposition and it consists of a reflection of the elements from one side of the principal diagonal (i.e. that through a_{11}, a_{22}, ...) to the other side. This has the effect of turning rows into columns and columns into rows. As for vectors, this operation is denoted by a tilde so that

$$\tilde{\boldsymbol{A}} = a_{ki} = \begin{pmatrix} a_{11} & a_{21} \dots a_{m1} \\ a_{12} & \\ \vdots & \\ a_{1n} & \dots a_{mn} \end{pmatrix} \tag{2.4.2}$$

The third operation combines these two operations. It is known as Hermitian conjugation and is denoted by a dagger so that

$$\boldsymbol{A}^\dagger = a_{ki}^* = \begin{pmatrix} a_{11}^* & a_{21}^* \cdots a_{m1}^* \\ a_{12}^* & \\ & \\ a_{1n}^* & \dots a_{mn}^* \end{pmatrix} \tag{2.4.3}$$

The three operations have a number of properties in common. Thus they all have a period of two since

$$(\boldsymbol{A}^*)^* = \boldsymbol{A}, \quad \tilde{\tilde{\boldsymbol{A}}} = \boldsymbol{A}, \quad (\boldsymbol{A}^\dagger)^\dagger = \boldsymbol{A} \tag{2.4.4}$$

They also behave similarly under addition and scalar multiplication

$$\begin{gathered}(\boldsymbol{A}+\boldsymbol{B})^* = \boldsymbol{A}^* + \boldsymbol{B}^*, \quad \widetilde{(\boldsymbol{A}+\boldsymbol{B})} = \tilde{\boldsymbol{A}} + \tilde{\boldsymbol{B}} \\ (\boldsymbol{A}+\boldsymbol{B})^\dagger = \boldsymbol{A}^\dagger + \boldsymbol{B}^\dagger\end{gathered} \tag{2.4.5}$$

$$(\lambda\boldsymbol{A})^* = \lambda^*\boldsymbol{A}^*, \quad \widetilde{(\lambda\boldsymbol{A})} = \lambda\tilde{\boldsymbol{A}}, \quad (\lambda\boldsymbol{A})^\dagger = \lambda^*\boldsymbol{A}^\dagger \tag{2.4.6}$$

The effect of transposing the product of a matrix and a vector gives something unexpected; for if

$$\boldsymbol{y} = \boldsymbol{A}\boldsymbol{x}$$

then

$$\begin{aligned}(y_1 y_2 \,..\, y_m) &= (a_{11}x_1 + a_{12}x_2 + \ldots a_{1n}x_n, a_{21}x_1 + \ldots, \\ &\qquad \ldots, a_{m1}x_1 + \ldots a_{mn}x_n) \\ &= (x_1 a_{11} + x_2 a_{12} + \ldots x_n a_{1n}, x_1 a_{21} + \ldots, \\ &\qquad \ldots, x_1 a_{m1} + \ldots x_n a_{mn})\end{aligned} \tag{2.4.7}$$

so that

$$\tilde{\boldsymbol{y}} = \tilde{\boldsymbol{x}}\tilde{\boldsymbol{A}} \tag{2.4.8}$$

Similarly, for the other operations, it can be shown that

$$\boldsymbol{y}^\dagger = \boldsymbol{x}^\dagger\boldsymbol{A}^\dagger \tag{2.4.9}$$

but

$$\boldsymbol{y}^* = \boldsymbol{A}^*\boldsymbol{x}^* \tag{2.4.10}$$

The matrix product behaves in the same way since it consists of operations of the same type and so

$$\widetilde{(\boldsymbol{AB})} = \tilde{\boldsymbol{B}}\tilde{\boldsymbol{A}}, \quad (\boldsymbol{AB})^* = \boldsymbol{A}^*\boldsymbol{B}^*, \quad (\boldsymbol{AB})^\dagger = \boldsymbol{B}^\dagger\boldsymbol{A}^\dagger \tag{2.4.11}$$

It often happens that the effect of one of these operations leaves a matrix unaltered or changed only in sign. When this happens the matrix is given a distinctive adjective which describes the property. These adjectives are given in this list:

$\boldsymbol{A} = \boldsymbol{A}^*$	real,	$\boldsymbol{A} = -\boldsymbol{A}^*$	imaginary
$\boldsymbol{A} = \tilde{\boldsymbol{A}}$	symmetric,	$\boldsymbol{A} = -\tilde{\boldsymbol{A}}$	antisymmetric or skew
$\boldsymbol{A} = \boldsymbol{A}^\dagger$	Hermitian,	$\boldsymbol{A} = -\boldsymbol{A}^\dagger$	antihermitian

2.5 Reciprocal Matrices

A square matrix, i.e. one with $m = n$, can be multiplied by itself to give its square

$$\boldsymbol{A}^2 = \boldsymbol{AA} \tag{2.5.1}$$

and similarly any positive integral power can be calculated. The question then arises whether it is possible to find the negative powers and, in particular, whether a matrix $\boldsymbol{A}$ has a reciprocal $\boldsymbol{A}^{-1}$ satisfying

$$\boldsymbol{AA}^{-1} = \boldsymbol{A}^{-1}\boldsymbol{A} = \boldsymbol{I} \tag{2.5.2}$$

This would also enable processes similar to division to be applied to matrices.

For the 2×2 matrix

$$\boldsymbol{A} = \begin{pmatrix} a & b \\ c & d \end{pmatrix} \tag{2.5.3}$$

it is easy to verify that the reciprocal matrix is

$$\boldsymbol{A}^{-1} = \begin{pmatrix} d & -b \\ -c & a \end{pmatrix} \Big/ (ad - bc) \tag{2.5.4}$$

This example is enough to suggest that reciprocals of matrices often exist and can be evaluated in terms of the original matrix but it also shows that there are exceptions. Thus if

$$\begin{vmatrix} a & b \\ c & d \end{vmatrix} = (ad - bc) = 0 \tag{2.5.5}$$

then the expression breaks down. Matrices whose determinants vanish are called singular and do not have reciprocals. Matrices whose determinants do not vanish are non-singular and can be proved always to have reciprocals. Practical methods of calculating reciprocal matrices are discussed in chapter 3.

Occasionally there is a very simple relation between a matrix and its reciprocal and since these matrices have distinctive properties it is useful to have adjectives for them. The most common types are the

self-reciprocal	$\boldsymbol{A}^{-1} = \boldsymbol{A}$
orthogonal	$\boldsymbol{A}^{-1} = \tilde{\boldsymbol{A}}$
unitary	$\boldsymbol{A}^{-1} = \boldsymbol{A}^\dagger$

2.6 Matrix Series

Knowledge of the powers of a matrix enables polynomial functions of a matrix to be evaluated and leads naturally to the study of infinite series of matrices. Obviously, the sum of any finite number of terms in the series can be calculated but the result has a meaning only if the process converges. It is necessary then that every component in the matrix of the sum should converge. The tests used to prove convergence are discussed in 4.11.

Many of the series familiar in ordinary analysis also apply to matrices even though the tests for convergence differ. One familiar series is the geometric series

$$1 + x + x^2 + \ldots = 1/(1 - x) \tag{2.6.1}$$

and for matrices the corresponding result is

$$\boldsymbol{I} + \boldsymbol{A} + \boldsymbol{A}^2 + \ldots = (\boldsymbol{I} - \boldsymbol{A})^{-1} \tag{2.6.2}$$

This can be proved by the same method as for the numerical series and the series converges if, as n becomes large, $\boldsymbol{A}^n$ approaches $\boldsymbol{O}$.

This series can be used as the basis of a method of calculating a reciprocal matrix. Similarly the exponential series suggests that $\exp(\boldsymbol{A})$ should be defined as

$$\exp(\boldsymbol{A}) = \boldsymbol{I} + \boldsymbol{A} + \boldsymbol{A}^2/2! + \boldsymbol{A}^3/3! + \ldots \tag{2.6.3}$$

and also the related series such as

$$\sin \boldsymbol{A} = \boldsymbol{A} - \boldsymbol{A}^3/3! + \ldots \tag{2.6.4}$$

$$\cosh \boldsymbol{A} = \boldsymbol{I} + \boldsymbol{A}^2/2! + \ldots \tag{2.6.5}$$

From the binomial theorem is derived series such as

$$(\boldsymbol{I} - \boldsymbol{A})^{\frac{1}{2}} = \boldsymbol{I} - \tfrac{1}{2}\boldsymbol{A} - \tfrac{3}{8}\boldsymbol{A}^2 - \ldots \tag{2.6.6}$$

though here again the series can be used only when it converges.

Some of the properties of the functions defined by the numerical series can also be established for the matrix functions but often there are restrictions and sometimes there is no analogous property. There has, therefore, to be a careful investigation before any property of the numerical series is assumed to hold for the matrix series. Thus, for example, the exponential property

$$\exp(\boldsymbol{A}) \exp(\boldsymbol{B}) = \exp(\boldsymbol{A} + \boldsymbol{B}) \tag{2.6.7}$$

holds for matrices only when

$$\boldsymbol{AB} = \boldsymbol{BA} \tag{2.6.8}$$

2.7 Partitioning and Bordering

It often becomes necessary, because of the size of a matrix, to divide it into submatrices in order to be able to handle it conveniently. Sometimes, too, even for smaller matrices, this division will illuminate the properties of the matrix. The division of a matrix into row or column vectors, in (2.3.15) and (2.3.18) is one example of this. The division is carried out by means of horizontal or vertical partitions dividing the whole matrix. The positions of the partitions have to be chosen so that the submatrices can be added or multiplied as the context requires. Thus two matrices partitioned at exactly the same places are added by adding the submatrices, e.g.

$$\begin{pmatrix} \mathbf{A} & \mathbf{B} \\ \mathbf{C} & \mathbf{D} \end{pmatrix} + \begin{pmatrix} \mathbf{X} & \mathbf{Y} \\ \mathbf{Z} & \mathbf{W} \end{pmatrix} = \begin{pmatrix} \mathbf{A}+\mathbf{X} & \mathbf{B}+\mathbf{Y} \\ \mathbf{C}+\mathbf{Z} & \mathbf{D}+\mathbf{W} \end{pmatrix} \tag{2.7.1}$$

On the other hand, for two partitioned matrices to be multiplied the vertical partitions of the first must match the horizontal partitions of the second so that the orders of the submatrices may be correct in each of the submatrix products. The rule for multiplication is exactly analogous to that for matrices except that the elements are now submatrices and the order in which they are multiplied is important. This rule is readily verified by expanding the matrix products. If one matrix, for example, is partitioned as

$$\begin{pmatrix} \mathbf{A} & \mathbf{B} \\ \mathbf{C} & \mathbf{D} \end{pmatrix} = \begin{pmatrix} a_{11} & a_{12} \dots a_{1n} & b_{11} \dots b_{1p} \\ \vdots & & \vdots \\ a_{m1} & \dots \quad a_{mn} & b_{m1} \dots b_{mp} \\ c_{11} & \dots \quad c_{1n} & d_{11} \dots d_{1p} \\ \vdots & & \\ c_{q1} & \dots \quad c_{qn} & d_{q1} \dots d_{qp} \end{pmatrix} \tag{2.7.2}$$

and a second as

$$\begin{pmatrix} \mathbf{E} & \mathbf{F} \\ \mathbf{G} & \mathbf{H} \end{pmatrix} = \begin{pmatrix} e_{11} \dots e_{1r} & f_{11} \dots f_{1s} \\ \vdots & \\ e_{n1} \dots e_{nr} & f_{n1} \dots f_{ns} \\ g_{11} \dots g_{1r} & h_{11} \dots h_{1s} \\ \vdots & \\ g_{p1} \dots g_{pr} & h_{p1} \dots h_{ps} \end{pmatrix} \tag{2.7.3}$$

then they can be multiplied to give

$$\begin{pmatrix} \mathbf{A} & \mathbf{B} \\ \mathbf{C} & \mathbf{D} \end{pmatrix} \begin{pmatrix} \mathbf{E} & \mathbf{F} \\ \mathbf{G} & \mathbf{H} \end{pmatrix} = \begin{pmatrix} \mathbf{AE}+\mathbf{BG} & \mathbf{AF}+\mathbf{BH} \\ \mathbf{CE}+\mathbf{DG} & \mathbf{CF}+\mathbf{DH} \end{pmatrix} \tag{2.7.4}$$

As an example of the value of partitioning consider the problem of finding the reciprocal of a matrix. If the matrix is partitioned as

$$\begin{pmatrix} \boldsymbol{A} & \boldsymbol{B} \\ \boldsymbol{C} & \boldsymbol{D} \end{pmatrix}$$

where $\boldsymbol{A}$ and $\boldsymbol{D}$ are square and non-singular then the inverse matrix can be shown by direct multiplication to be

$$\begin{pmatrix} \boldsymbol{A} & \boldsymbol{B} \\ \boldsymbol{C} & \boldsymbol{D} \end{pmatrix}^{-1} = \begin{pmatrix} (\boldsymbol{A} - \boldsymbol{B}\boldsymbol{D}^{-1}\boldsymbol{C})^{-1} & -\boldsymbol{A}^{-1}\boldsymbol{B}(\boldsymbol{D} - \boldsymbol{C}\boldsymbol{A}^{-1}\boldsymbol{B})^{-1} \\ -\boldsymbol{D}^{-1}\boldsymbol{C}(\boldsymbol{A} - \boldsymbol{B}\boldsymbol{D}^{-1}\boldsymbol{C})^{-1} & (\boldsymbol{D} - \boldsymbol{C}\boldsymbol{A}^{-1}\boldsymbol{B})^{-1} \end{pmatrix} \tag{2.7.5}$$

The original problem is thus reduced to that of finding the reciprocals of $\boldsymbol{A}, \boldsymbol{D}, (\boldsymbol{A} - \boldsymbol{B}\boldsymbol{D}^{-1}\boldsymbol{C})$ and $(\boldsymbol{D} - \boldsymbol{C}\boldsymbol{A}^{-1}\boldsymbol{B})$ and, since these are of smaller order, this may well be an easier task.

The process known as bordering a matrix is similar in kind to partitioning. It consists in adding matrices or vectors to a matrix to enlarge it. The enlarged matrix can then be partitioned into the original matrix and its borders. The relations between the orders of the submatrices of this partitioned matrix give then the relations that must exist between the order of the original matrix and its border. If, for example, a vector is defined by the equation

$$\boldsymbol{y} = \boldsymbol{A}\boldsymbol{x} + \boldsymbol{z} \tag{2.7.6}$$

the mixture of addition and multiplication may be inconvenient but, by defining the bordered matrix $\boldsymbol{B}$ as

$$\boldsymbol{B} = (\boldsymbol{A}\boldsymbol{z}) = \begin{pmatrix} a_{11} & \dots & a_{1n} & z_1 \\ \vdots & & & \\ a_{m1} & \dots & a_{mn} & z_m \end{pmatrix} \tag{2.7.7}$$

and

$$\boldsymbol{w} = \begin{pmatrix} \boldsymbol{x} \\ 1 \end{pmatrix} \tag{2.7.8}$$

it takes the simpler form

$$\boldsymbol{y} = \boldsymbol{B}\boldsymbol{w} \tag{2.7.9}$$

In general, bordering helps not only to condense and simplify the notation of equations such as these but also to lead to unified techniques of calculation using the equations.

2.8 Direct Products

In addition to the scalar and vector products of two vectors there is a third type of product known as their direct product†. The components

† Alternative names are the outer, tensor or Kronecker product.

of the direct product are found by multiplying the components of the two vectors together in all possible ways. If the first vector has m components a_i and the second n components b_k the direct product has mn components and is best arranged as a matrix

$$a_i b_k = f_{ik} \tag{2.8.1}$$

In symbolic form the direct product can still be indicated by matrix multiplication and (1) becomes

$$\boldsymbol{a}\tilde{\boldsymbol{b}} = \boldsymbol{F} \tag{2.8.2}$$

The order of the two factors and the row-by-column rule of matrix multiplication ensure that the direct product is distinguished from the scalar product $\tilde{\boldsymbol{a}}\boldsymbol{b}$. The sum of the diagonal elements of the direct product, however, does give the scalar product. Since the direct product is a particular kind of matrix product the rules of matrix multiplication, given in 2.3, apply equally to it.

The geometrical significance of the direct product can be illustrated by considering its effect on another vector. If $\boldsymbol{a}$ is a unit vector then the direct product of $\boldsymbol{a}$ with itself is

$$\boldsymbol{a}\tilde{\boldsymbol{a}}$$

and when this acts on a vector $\boldsymbol{c}$ the result is a vector

$$\boldsymbol{d} = \boldsymbol{a}(\tilde{\boldsymbol{a}}\boldsymbol{c}) \tag{2.8.3}$$

which has the same direction as $\boldsymbol{a}$ but with magnitude $|\boldsymbol{c}| \cos \theta$ so that $\boldsymbol{d}$ is the projection of $\boldsymbol{c}$ on to $\boldsymbol{a}$. The direct square thus gives a projection operator. One characteristic property of a projection operator P is that it gives the same result when repeated, i.e.

$$P^2 = P \tag{2.8.4}$$

The more general product also satisfies this equation when

$$\tilde{\boldsymbol{b}}\boldsymbol{a} = 1 \tag{2.8.5}$$

for then

$$(\boldsymbol{a}\tilde{\boldsymbol{b}})(\boldsymbol{a}\tilde{\boldsymbol{b}}) = \boldsymbol{a}(\tilde{\boldsymbol{b}}\boldsymbol{a})\tilde{\boldsymbol{b}} = \boldsymbol{a}\tilde{\boldsymbol{b}} \tag{2.8.6}$$

Thus $\boldsymbol{a}\tilde{\boldsymbol{b}}$ may also be called a projection operator since it gives a vector in the same fixed direction as $\boldsymbol{a}$ but with magnitude depending on the scalar product on to $\boldsymbol{b}$.

Other direct products, of a matrix and a vector for instance, can be constructed but the results are higher order tensors and cannot be expressed in matrix notation. They are treated in chapter 5.

EXERCISES

1. Prove

$$\begin{pmatrix} 2 & 1 \\ -3 & 4 \end{pmatrix}\begin{pmatrix} 1 & 0 & 2 \\ 4 & 2 & 3 \end{pmatrix} = \begin{pmatrix} 6 & 2 & 7 \\ 13 & 8 & 6 \end{pmatrix}$$

2. Classify

$$\begin{pmatrix} 0 & i \\ i & 0 \end{pmatrix}, \begin{pmatrix} 1 & 2 \\ 2 & 3 \end{pmatrix}, \begin{pmatrix} 2 & 1-i \\ 1+i & 5 \end{pmatrix}, \begin{pmatrix} 3 & 1-i \\ -1+i & 0 \end{pmatrix}, \begin{pmatrix} 2 & 1 \\ -1 & 4 \end{pmatrix}$$

3. Show that a matrix which satisfies two of the symmetry relations of 2.4 is one of the four types

	A	A^*	$\tilde{A}$	$A^\dagger$
real Hermitian	1	1	1	1
imaginary symmetric	1	−1	1	−1
real skew	1	1	−1	−1
imaginary Hermitian	1	−1	−1	1

4. Show that the matrices for S_x, S_y, S_z are all Hermitian and that

$$S_x^2 = S_y^2 = S_z^2 = \tfrac{1}{4}I$$

5. Prove that

$$(AB)^* = A^*B^*, \quad (AB)^\dagger = B^\dagger A^\dagger, \quad (AB)^{-1} = B^{-1}A^{-1}$$

6. Show that $E_{ij}E_{lm} = E_{im}\delta_{jl}$.

7. Verify that

$$(I - \alpha E_{ij} - \beta E_{lm})^{-1} = I + \alpha E_{ij} + \beta E_{lm}$$

provided that $i \neq j,\ j \neq l,\ l \neq m,\ m \neq i$

8. Show that

$$\exp\begin{pmatrix} 0 & i\theta \\ i\theta & 0 \end{pmatrix} = \begin{pmatrix} \cos\theta & i\sin\theta \\ i\sin\theta & \cos\theta \end{pmatrix}, \quad \exp\begin{pmatrix} 0 & 0 & 0 \\ 2 & 0 & 0 \\ 4 & 2 & 0 \end{pmatrix} = \begin{pmatrix} 1 & 0 & 0 \\ 2 & 1 & 0 \\ 6 & 2 & 1 \end{pmatrix}$$

9. If v has components dv_i/dt show that the solution of the linear differential equations $\dot{v} = Av$ is $v = e^{tA}v_0$.

10. Find the reciprocals and show that

$$\begin{pmatrix} 2 & 3 \\ -1 & 3 \end{pmatrix}^{-1} = \tfrac{1}{9}\begin{pmatrix} 3 & -3 \\ 1 & 2 \end{pmatrix}, \quad \begin{pmatrix} 1 & 1 & 0 \\ 0 & 1 & 1 \\ 0 & 0 & 1 \end{pmatrix}^{-1} = \begin{pmatrix} 1 & -1 & 1 \\ 0 & 1 & -1 \\ 0 & 0 & 1 \end{pmatrix}$$

$$\begin{pmatrix} 1 & 1 & 0 \\ 0 & 1 & 1 \\ 1 & 0 & 1 \end{pmatrix}^{-1} = \tfrac{1}{2}\begin{pmatrix} 1 & -1 & 1 \\ 1 & 1 & -1 \\ -1 & 1 & 1 \end{pmatrix}, \quad \begin{pmatrix} 2 & 1 & 1 \\ 1 & 2 & 0 \\ 0 & 1 & 2 \end{pmatrix}^{-1} = \tfrac{1}{14}\begin{pmatrix} 8 & -1 & -3 \\ -4 & 4 & -2 \\ 2 & -2 & 8 \end{pmatrix}$$

$$\begin{pmatrix} 2 & 4 & 5 \\ 0 & 1 & 6 \\ 0 & 0 & 3 \end{pmatrix}^{-1} = \tfrac{1}{6}\begin{pmatrix} 3 & -12 & 19 \\ 0 & 6 & -12 \\ 0 & 0 & 2 \end{pmatrix}$$

11. If the components of the basic vectors $\mathbf{e}_i$ are e_i prove that $E_{ij} = e_i\tilde{e}_j$, $a_{\cdot k} = Ae_k$, $a_{i\cdot} = \tilde{e}_iA$.

12. Prove that a matrix, other than I, which satisfies $P^2 = P$ has no reciprocal.

13. Prove that permutation matrices are orthogonal.

CHAPTER 3

LINEAR EQUATIONS

3.1 Introduction

The problem of solving a set of simultaneous linear equations in a number of variables (generally taken as n in this chapter) arises frequently in physics and chemistry. The elementary method of solution is to eliminate the variables from the equations one by one in an order suggested by the coefficients. Eventually an equation in one variable is obtained and from its solution the remaining variables are found quickly, by substituting in turn into the intermediate equations. This method, though correct in principle, has a number of disadvantages in practice. In the first place, it is not systematic enough to be a good numerical method. A method which works satisfactorily when the coefficients are integers, may be cumbersome and difficult to check when the coefficients are unwieldy decimals. In the second place, it is difficult to subject it to theoretical analysis so as to understand complications, such as mounting rounding-off errors or ill-conditioning, which arise occasionally in practice. The first object of this chapter is to give a systematic method of eliminating the variables and solving the equations and then to discuss the various difficulties that may arise. There is also a short account of some alternative methods of solution which may be simpler and easier to apply in certain circumstances.

3.2 The Condensed Elimination Method

If the first two equations of the set are written with the notation

$$a_{11}x_1 + a_{12}x_2 + \ldots = a_{1\,n+1} \tag{3.2.1}$$

$$a_{21}x_1 + a_{22}x_2 + \ldots = a_{2\,n+1} \tag{3.2.2}$$

and, if necessary, their order adjusted so that the coefficient a_{11} is non-zero then the first equation can be used to eliminate x_1 from the second. This can be done in various ways and one convenient choice is to multiply the first equation by a_{21}/a_{11} and subtract from the second leaving

$$\left(a_{22} - \frac{a_{21}}{a_{11}} a_{12}\right)x_2 + \left(a_{23} - \frac{a_{21}}{a_{11}} a_{13}\right)x_3 + \dots = \left(a_{2\ n+1} - \frac{a_{21}}{a_{11}} a_{1\ n+1}\right) \tag{3.2.3}$$

This is the basic step in the elimination method and it is repeated in an extended form to eliminate the remaining variables. It simplifies the notation and helps to clarify later equations if (3) is now written as

$$b_{22}x_2 + b_{23}x_3 + \dots = b_{2\ n+1} \tag{3.2.4}$$

with the definition

$$b_{ij} = a_{ij} - \frac{a_{i1}}{a_{11}} a_{1j} \tag{3.2.5}$$

The third equation of the set is

$$a_{31}x_1 + a_{32}x_2 + a_{33}x_3 + \dots = a_{3\ n+1} \tag{3.2.6}$$

and both x_1 and x_2 are to be eliminated from it. The first equation (1) is multiplied by a_{31}/a_{11} and subtracted from (6) to eliminate x_1 as in (5). To eliminate x_2, (4) is used, instead of (2), since it does not reintroduce x_1. It is multiplied by b_{32}/b_{22} and subtracted from the previous result to give

$$c_{33}x_3 + c_{34}x_4 + \dots = c_{3\ n+1} \tag{3.2.7}$$

where now the two eliminations can be performed together by defining

$$c_{ij} = a_{ij} - \frac{a_{i1}}{a_{11}} a_{1j} - \frac{b_{i2}}{b_{22}} b_{2j} \tag{3.2.8}$$

In this way the original equations are reduced to the triangular set (1), (4), (7), ... and the number of variables steadily decreases. The nth equation contains only a single variable, x_n, and is solved by simple division. This value of the variable is then inserted into the penultimate equation of the triangular set to yield x_{n-1}. The remaining variables follow in turn by substituting into the triangular equations in reverse order.

One major advantage of this systematic method is that the number of quantities which need to be recorded is drastically reduced. The quantities needed for the elimination or the substitution are the multipliers and the triangular equations and these can be written as

$$\begin{array}{llll} & & a_{11}x_1 + a_{12}x_2 + a_{13}x_3 + \dots & = a_{1\,n+1} \\ \dfrac{a_{21}}{a_{11}}, & & b_{22}x_2 + b_{23}x_3 + \dots & = b_{2\,n+1} \\ \dfrac{a_{31}}{a_{11}}, & \dfrac{b_{32}}{b_{22}}, & c_{33}x_3 + \dots & = c_{3\,n+1}, \text{ etc.} \end{array} \qquad (3.2.9)$$

where the multipliers are noted beside the equation requiring them. This scheme can be reduced still further by omitting the variables which only serve to label the numbers and the algebraic signs which can be readily understood. The coefficients are now identified by the row and column in which they appear and form the rectangular array

$$\begin{array}{lllll} a_{11} & a_{12} & a_{13} & \dots & a_{1\,n+1} \\ \dfrac{a_{21}}{a_{11}} & b_{22} & b_{23} & \dots & b_{2\,n+1} \\ \dfrac{a_{31}}{a_{11}} & \dfrac{b_{32}}{b_{22}} & c_{33} & \dots & c_{3\,n+1} \\ \vdots & & & & \\ \dfrac{a_{n1}}{a_{11}} & \dfrac{b_{n2}}{b_{22}} & \dfrac{c_{n3}}{c_{33}} & \dots & n_{n\,n+1} \\ x_1 & x_2 & x_3 & \dots & \end{array} \qquad (3.2.10)$$

and the solutions are written in the columns to which they refer, as they are found. The numbers in this array are calculated in shells in the sequence indicated in Fig. 3.1.

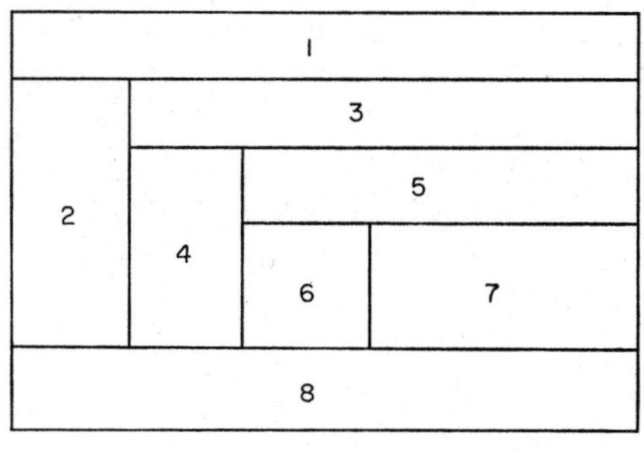

FIG. 3.1. Sequence of calculation of elements.

Equations such as (5) and (8) prescribe how the numbers are calculated and these reduce to an easily remembered procedure when translated into terms of the array. Each term above the principal diagonal is found by taking the corresponding coefficient in the original equations and subtracting the scalar product of the other elements to its left side in the same row in the new array with the other elements above it in the same column, corresponding components being located at the same distance from the edges. The vectors used for the element at X are indicated in Fig. 3.2. An element below the diagonal is calculated by

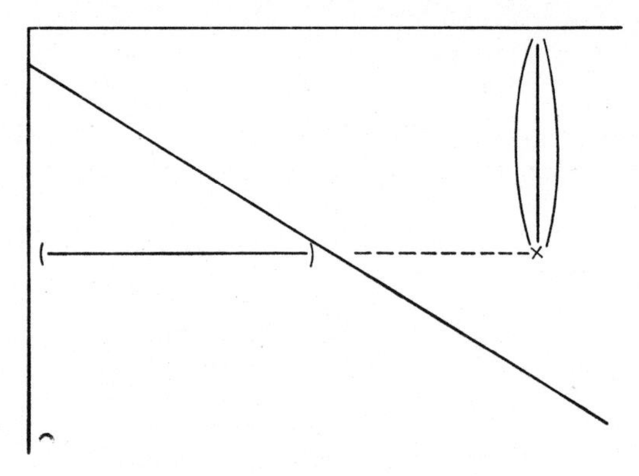

FIG. 3.2. Row and column vectors used to form X.

the same procedure except that each element is divided by the diagonal element above it. The rules for substituting and solving for the variables can be similarly expressed in terms of the scalar product of the rows of the triangular equations and the final row of solutions but are more easily remembered by noting that (10) is equivalent to the triangular set of equations in (9).

A numerical procedure of this type needs to have adequate checks which will ensure that errors are discovered as quickly as possible and that the solution may be proved correct. The only way of guaranteeing the solution is to substitute it into the original equations and to show that they are satisfied to within the allowable rounding-off error but, if this final check should fail, there is no indication of where the error lurks. It is necessary, therefore, to supplement this final check with a running check which provides some control over the calculation at intermediate stages. This is done by the simple device of changing the variables to the new variables

$$\bar{x}_i = x_i + 1 \tag{3.2.11}$$

The equations for these new variables are identical with those for the original variables except that the constants on the right are now the sum of all the coefficients in the original equations. These constants are denoted by

$$a_{i\,n+2} = a_{i1} + a_{i2} + \dots + a_{i\,n+1} \tag{3.2.12}$$

and are written as an extra column beside the original equations. In the new array produced by the elimination the corresponding new column is found by the same rules as before. Each element of this new column provides a check. Thus, after x_1 has been eliminated, (11) implies the relation

$$b_{2\,n+2} = b_{22} + b_{23} + \dots + b_{2\,n+1} \tag{3.2.13}$$

and this can be checked. Each row of the new array is subject in this way to the check that the sum of the elements from the diagonal one to the $(n + 1)$th should equal the $(n + 2)$th. There is also a check on the final stages of the solution for, if the final column is used instead of the $(n + 1)$th, the values of $\bar{x}_i$ can be found and used to check the values of x_i. This running check gives no guarantee of the final result and so does not replace the substitution check. It should be considered as a method of spotting the most likely errors as they occur. It also gives an indication of the magnitude of the rounding-off errors.

In Table 3.1 an example of this condensed method is worked out. On the left is a key indicating the notation used above for the entries on the right.

TABLE 3.1

Condensed elimination method

$$\begin{array}{rcl} 2w + x - y & = & 5 \\ 2w + 4x + y - 3z & = & 38 \\ -4w + 4x + 7y - 5z & = & 64 \\ 2w - 8x - 6y + 12z & = & -82 \end{array}$$

a_{11}	a_{12}	a_{13}	a_{14}	a_{15}	a_{16}	2	1	−1	0	5	7
a_{21}	a_{22}	a_{23}	a_{24}	a_{25}	a_{26}	2	4	1	−3	38	42
a_{31}	a_{32}	a_{33}	a_{34}	a_{35}	a_{36}	−4	4	7	−5	64	66
a_{41}	a_{42}	a_{43}	a_{44}	a_{45}	a_{46}	2	−8	−6	12	−82	−82

a_{11}	a_{12}	a_{13}	a_{14}	a_{15}	a_{16}	2	1	−1	0	5	7
a_{21}/a_{11}	b_{22}	b_{23}	b_{24}	b_{25}	b_{26}	1	3	2	−3	33	35
a_{31}/a_{11}	b_{32}/b_{22}	c_{33}	c_{34}	c_{35}	c_{36}	−2	2	1	1	8	10
a_{41}/a_{11}	b_{42}/b_{22}	c_{43}/c_{33}	d_{44}	d_{45}	d_{46}	1	−3	1	2	4	6
w	x	y	z			1	9	6	2		

3.3 Reciprocal Matrices

If two sets of equations differ only in the constants which appear on the right sides of the equations then, as has already been noted in section 3.2, the elimination of the variables leaves the left sides of the triangular equations exactly the same. The equations can then be solved simultaneously by treating the second set of constants as an extra column in the table. After the elimination stage this column is treated separately to give the second solution. This procedure is the same as that for the extra checking column and can be extended to any number of extra columns.

When there are a large number of sets of equations to be solved and they differ only in the constant terms there is a more economical procedure. Each set of equations can be written in matrix notation as

$$\boldsymbol{A}\boldsymbol{x} = \boldsymbol{c} \tag{3.3.1}$$

where $\boldsymbol{c}$ is the column vector of constants which changes with each set while $\boldsymbol{A}$ remains the same. The formal solution to this is found by multiplication by $\boldsymbol{A}^{-1}$, provided that $\boldsymbol{A}$ is non-singular, so that

$$\boldsymbol{x} = \boldsymbol{A}^{-1}\boldsymbol{c} \tag{3.3.2}$$

and once the matrix $\boldsymbol{A}^{-1}$ is known $\boldsymbol{x}$ is easily calculated for any $\boldsymbol{c}$. The equation defining $\boldsymbol{A}^{-1}$ is

$$\boldsymbol{A}\boldsymbol{A}^{-1} = \boldsymbol{I} \tag{3.3.3}$$

and this can be split up into n sets of equations for the n columns of $\boldsymbol{A}^{-1}$ so that

$$\begin{aligned} \boldsymbol{A}\boldsymbol{r}_1 &= \boldsymbol{e}_1 \\ \boldsymbol{A}\boldsymbol{r}_2 &= \boldsymbol{e}_2 \\ &\cdots\cdots \end{aligned} \tag{3.3.4}$$

where

$$\boldsymbol{A}^{-1} = (\boldsymbol{r}_1\boldsymbol{r}_2 \dots); \qquad \boldsymbol{I} = (\boldsymbol{e}_1\boldsymbol{e}_2 \dots) \tag{3.3.5}$$

The calculation of the reciprocal matrix in this way means solving n sets of equations each with the same coefficients on the left but with successive unit vectors on the right. These can be solved simultaneously and, if there are more than n sets of equations to be solved, it will clearly be more economical to find the reciprocal matrix and solve by a simple product with the various $\boldsymbol{c}$.

The accuracy of a calculated reciprocal matrix can be checked by multiplication into the original matrix in the reverse order

$$\boldsymbol{A}^{-1}\boldsymbol{A} = \boldsymbol{I} \tag{3.3.6}$$

A running check can also be provided, as before, by including an extra column which is the sum of all previous columns. The solutions found using this column will be

$$(\boldsymbol{r}_1 + \boldsymbol{r}_2 + \dots)_i + 1 \tag{3.3.7}$$

An example of the calculation of a reciprocal matrix is shown in Table 3.2 with this running check included. The elements of the reciprocal are denoted by r_{ij} and it is to be noted that the calculation produces them in transposed form.

TABLE 3.2

Inversion of a matrix

$$AI \quad \begin{pmatrix} 1 & 0 & -1 & 1 \\ 1 & 2 & 1 & -2 \\ -3 & -4 & 0 & 5 \\ 1 & 8 & 5 & -10 \end{pmatrix} \quad \begin{pmatrix} 1 & 0 & 0 & 0 \\ 0 & 1 & 0 & 0 \\ 0 & 0 & 1 & 0 \\ 0 & 0 & 0 & 1 \end{pmatrix} \quad \begin{matrix} -2 \\ 3 \\ -1 \\ 5 \end{matrix}$$

$$\begin{array}{rrrr|rrrr|r} 1 & 0 & -1 & 1 & 1 & 0 & 0 & 0 & 2 \\ 1 & 2 & 2 & -3 & -1 & 1 & 0 & 0 & 1 \\ -3 & -2 & 1 & 2 & 1 & 2 & 1 & 0 & 7 \\ 1 & 4 & -2 & 5 & 5 & 0 & 2 & 1 & 13 \end{array}$$

$$(\widetilde{A^{-1}}) \quad \begin{pmatrix} -1 & 2 & -1 & 1 \\ 2 & -1{\cdot}5 & 2 & 0 \\ -{\cdot}2 & {\cdot}4 & {\cdot}2 & {\cdot}4 \\ -{\cdot}6 & {\cdot}7 & -{\cdot}4 & {\cdot}2 \end{pmatrix}$$

Check

$$A^{-1}A = I \quad \begin{pmatrix} -1 & 2 & -{\cdot}2 & -{\cdot}6 \\ 2 & -1{\cdot}5 & {\cdot}4 & {\cdot}7 \\ -1 & 2 & {\cdot}2 & -{\cdot}4 \\ 1 & 0 & {\cdot}4 & {\cdot}2 \end{pmatrix} \begin{pmatrix} 1 & 0 & -1 & 1 \\ 1 & 2 & 1 & -2 \\ -3 & -4 & 0 & 5 \\ 1 & 8 & 5 & -10 \end{pmatrix} = \begin{pmatrix} 1 & 0 & 0 & 0 \\ 0 & 1 & 0 & 0 \\ 0 & 0 & 1 & 0 \\ 0 & 0 & 0 & 1 \end{pmatrix}$$

3.4 Difficulties

At several points in the description of this condensed form of the elimination method it has been assumed that various quantities do not vanish. In some circumstances this assumption breaks down and the method can be used with confidence only if these exceptions can be understood and appropriate techniques of handling them found.

The first of these quantities is a_{11}. Should a_{11} vanish, the elimination of x_1 fails since it involves dividing by a_{11}. This difficulty can always be overcome by rearranging either the order of the equations or the order of the variables. If a_{21}, for example, does not vanish then the first two equations are interchanged.

The second quantity is the second diagonal element in the triangular array, i.e. b_{22}. In terms of the original coefficients this quantity is the leading minor

$$b_{22} = \begin{vmatrix} a_{11} & a_{12} \\ a_{21} & a_{22} \end{vmatrix} \div a_{11} \tag{3.4.1}$$

and is always finite, since a_{11} does not vanish. It will vanish, however, if the 2×2 minor vanishes and this will cause difficulty when x_2 is being eliminated. To prevent b_{22} vanishing, it is still possible to replace the second equation by some other one or to renumber the variables. If necessary, the first equation can also be changed so that both the new a_{11} and b_{22} are non-zero. Thus, if any 2×2 minor in the matrix $\boldsymbol{A}$ is non-zero, the equations can be rearranged to satisfy these two requirements. If all the 2×2 minors vanish the matrix is said to have rank unity and further discussion of this is defered to section 3.5.

In a similar way, the third diagonal element can be shown to be

$$c_{33} = \begin{vmatrix} a_{11} & a_{12} & a_{13} \\ a_{21} & a_{22} & a_{23} \\ a_{31} & a_{32} & a_{33} \end{vmatrix} \div \begin{vmatrix} a_{11} & a_{12} \\ a_{21} & a_{22} \end{vmatrix} \tag{3.4.2}$$

and this, too, should not be zero if the elimination is to succeed. If there is one non-vanishing minor of order 3×3 then it is made into the principal one by rearrangements and, if necessary, rearrangements within the minor can be made to satisfy the earlier requirements. If all the 3×3 minors vanish but at least one 2×2 minor does not, the matrix is said to have rank two.

The general result, which can be proved by induction, is that the method assumes that the leading minors

$$a_{11}, \quad \begin{vmatrix} a_{11} & a_{12} \\ a_{21} & a_{22} \end{vmatrix}, \quad \begin{vmatrix} a_{11} & a_{12} & a_{13} \\ a_{21} & a_{22} & a_{23} \\ a_{31} & a_{32} & a_{33} \end{vmatrix}, \quad \ldots \quad \begin{vmatrix} a_{11} & \ldots & a_{1n} \\ a_{21} & & \\ \vdots & & \\ a_{n1} & \ldots & a_{nn} \end{vmatrix} \tag{3.4.3}$$

must all be non-zero, either in their natural order or after rearrangement of the equations and variables. The final minor is also the determinant $|\boldsymbol{A}|$ and a matrix, whose determinant is non-zero, is called non-singular. If $\boldsymbol{A}$ is non-singular it is easy to show, by using the expansion theorems, that at least one minor of each order is also non-zero, and so the necessary and sufficient condition for the equations to be solved by this method is that the matrix $\boldsymbol{A}$ be non-singular.

In the course of this discussion it has been shown in addition that

$$|\boldsymbol{A}| = a_{11}b_{22}c_{33} \ldots n_{nn} \tag{3.4.4}$$

This means that the condensed elimination method also gives an efficient method of evaluating a determinant by reducing it to triangular form and multiplying the diagonal elements.

In practice, it is very rare for a minor to vanish exactly since the calculations are carried out to a limited accuracy only and rounding-off errors can disguise the zero. The situation is not greatly different, however, when one of the leading minors becomes of the same order as the rounding-off error. Even though the method can be continued formally, the error caused by dividing by this small minor will be so large as to make further work of little value. It is highly desirable, therefore, that none of the leading minors should be small. If the matrix is non-singular this can be ensured by rearrangements of the type already mentioned but this procedure can be tedious and may not be necessary. It is more useful to have a practical compromise which will reduce the chance of finding a small leading minor at the expense of rearrangements which can be carried out easily in advance. The following rules embody such a compromise:

(a) The largest coefficients in the equations are made of comparable magnitude by multiplying the equations throughout by suitable factors and by replacing the variables by others proportional to them. This should be done before any rounding off. The simplest factors are usually powers of ten.

(b) Two equations, whose coefficients are almost the same, should be replaced by two new equations, one found by adding the equations and the other by subtracting them and rescaling.

(c) The orders of the equations and of the variables are then adjusted to bring the largest coefficients (irrespective of sign) into the diagonal positions and the smallest coefficients as far as possible into the positions below the diagonal.

Another way in which this difficulty becomes evident is when, even though a solution has been correctly obtained, it gives considerable residuals, due to rounding-off error, when substituted into the original equations. There is a simple way of improving such a solution. If the solution is denoted by $\bar{x}_i$ and the true solution is

$$x_i = \bar{x}_i + \bar{\bar{x}}_i \tag{3.4.5}$$

where $\bar{x}_i$ are small corrections, then, by substitution into the original equations

$$A\bar{\bar{x}} = r \tag{3.4.6}$$

where the components of r are the residuals

$$r_i = -a_{i1}\bar{x}_1 - a_{i2}\bar{x}_2 - \ldots + a_{i\ n+1} \tag{3.4.7}$$

The set of equations (6) has the same matrix A as before and so its solution involves only the addition of an extra column to the previous calculation and the computation of the $\bar{\bar{x}}_i$. The same procedure can be applied if, after the calculation has been completed, it is desired to carry the solution to a larger number of decimals.

3.5 Rank

The definition of matrices of rank one and two has been mentioned in 3.4 and can now be generalized to arbitrary rank. If all the $(r + 1)$th order minors, that can be formed from a matrix by omitting rows and columns, have the value zero and at least one minor of rth order has a non-zero value then the rank of the matrix is said to be r. When the rank is less than n, the order of the matrix A, the elimination procedure breaks down. A full analysis of the resulting situation is given in various textbooks and only the principal results will be mentioned here.

If a matrix has rank less than n it means that the expressions on the left sides of the equations are no longer independent. In other words it is possible to multiply the equations by selected constants and find that the sum of $(n - 1)$ of them has the same left side as the remaining equation. There are, then, two different possibilities according as the right side of this sum is equal to, or different from, that of the other equations. If the two right sides differ, by more than the rounding-off error, then the equations are inconsistent and no solution is possible. If the two right sides are equal, then the information about the variables, contained in the final equation, is already contained in the other equations. In consequence there is no longer sufficient information in the equations to determine all the variables uniquely.

The number of independent expressions on the left of the equations is given by the rank of A. If the matrix, formed by bordering A with the column of constants on the right, has the same rank as A then this is also the number of independent equations available. The equations are inconsistent if the ranks are not equal. When the number of independent equations is less than the number of variables then the solution is not unique and the remaining variables can be assigned arbitrary values. The elimination method can be broken off, therefore, when the number of triangular equations equals the rank and the solution is completed giving arbitrary values to the variables not determined by these equations.

3.6 Homogeneous Equations

All the equations in the previous parts of this chapter are inhomogeneous, in the sense that at least one of the equations in the set contains a non-zero constant term as well as the terms containing the unknown variables. If all these constant terms vanish, the equations are said to be homogeneous and their solution needs further discussion.

In contrast to a set of inhomogeneous equations, a set of homogeneous equations never has a unique solution. For, if x_i is one solution, then kx_i is also a solution, for any value of the constant k. In particular, these equations always have the trivial solution

$$x_i = 0 \tag{3.6.1}$$

Because of the circumstances in which these equations arise, this lack of uniqueness rarely has any significance and the solution is made unique by adding some extra inhomogeneous restriction. The two most common restrictions are either to fix the value of one variable at unity or, alternatively, to adjust all the variables so that the sum of their squares is unity. The first method is usually easier for numerical purposes. Another way of describing it is to say that the equations have been divided throughout by the selected variable and so become a set of n inhomogeneous equations in $(n - 1)$ new variables which are the ratios of the old variables to the selected one. In general, therefore, the variables are overdetermined and the only solution is the trivial one (1). To have a non-trivial solution, one of the equations in the set must be linearly dependent on the others. The condition that this should be so, for the set of equations

$$\boldsymbol{A}\boldsymbol{x} = 0 \tag{3.6.2}$$

is that

$$|\boldsymbol{A}| = 0 \tag{3.6.3}$$

Thus for a set of homogeneous equations to have a non-trivial solution which is unique, except for an arbitrary constant k, the matrix $\boldsymbol{A}$ must have rank $(n - 1)$. If the rank is less than $(n - 1)$, the solutions will also show the lack of uniqueness discussed in section 3.5.

3.7 Factorization of a Matrix into Triangular Matrices

The theoretical significance of the first stage in the elimination process is that, by a limited number of operations, the original matrix $\boldsymbol{A}$ of the equations is turned into a triangular matrix $\boldsymbol{T}$ whose elements below the leading diagonal are all zero. To clarify and extend this result, it is convenient to express the operations in terms of matrices.

The first operation in the elimination is to remove x_1 from the second equation by subtracting a_{21}/a_{11} times the first equation from it. This is equivalent to the product

$$(\boldsymbol{I} - a_{21}/a_{11}\boldsymbol{E}_{21})\boldsymbol{A} \tag{3.7.1}$$

The elimination of x_1 from all the equations is achieved by the operator

$$\boldsymbol{I} - (a_{21}\boldsymbol{E}_{21} + a_{31}\boldsymbol{E}_{31} + \dots)/a_{11} \tag{3.7.2}$$

premultiplied into $\boldsymbol{A}$. The variable x_2 is eliminated in the same way using

$$\boldsymbol{I} - (b_{32}\boldsymbol{E}_{32} + b_{42}\boldsymbol{E}_{42} + \dots)/b_{22} \tag{3.7.3}$$

The whole process of reduction to $\boldsymbol{T}$ is then represented by

$$\boldsymbol{KA} = \boldsymbol{T} \tag{3.7.4}$$

where the matrix $\boldsymbol{K}$ has the product form

$$\begin{aligned}\boldsymbol{K} = [&\boldsymbol{I} - m_{n\ n-1}\boldsymbol{E}_{n\ n-1}/m_{n-1\ n-1}] \dots \\ &[\boldsymbol{I} - (b_{32}\boldsymbol{E}_{32} + \dots)/b_{22}][\boldsymbol{I} - (a_{21}\boldsymbol{E}_{21} + \dots)/a_{11}]\end{aligned} \tag{3.7.5}$$

A more convenient form of this relation between $\boldsymbol{A}$ and $\boldsymbol{T}$ can be found by using the reciprocal of $\boldsymbol{K}$. It is easily shown that

$$|\boldsymbol{K}| = 1 \tag{3.7.6}$$

and consequently $\boldsymbol{K}$ is non-singular and has a reciprocal. Since $\boldsymbol{K}$ is a product, its reciprocal is the product of the reciprocals of each factor, taken in the reverse order. The individual factors are easily inverted according to the rule

See #7, p. 34.

$$[\boldsymbol{I} - \alpha\boldsymbol{E}_{r+1\ r} - \beta\boldsymbol{E}_{r+2\ r} - \dots]^{-1} = \boldsymbol{I} + \alpha\boldsymbol{E}_{r+1\ r} + \beta\boldsymbol{E}_{r+2\ r} + \dots \tag{3.7.7}$$

which can be proved by multiplication. This gives

$$\begin{aligned}\boldsymbol{K}^{-1} &= [\boldsymbol{I} + (a_{21}\boldsymbol{E}_{21} + \dots)/a_{11}][\boldsymbol{I} + (b_{32}\boldsymbol{E}_{32} + .)/b_{22}] \dots \\ &= \boldsymbol{I} + (a_{21}\boldsymbol{E}_{21} + \dots)/a_{11} + (b_{32}\boldsymbol{E}_{32} + \dots)/b_{22} + \dots\end{aligned} \tag{3.7.8}$$

which can be written as

$$\boldsymbol{K}^{-1} = \boldsymbol{I} + \boldsymbol{L} \tag{3.7.9}$$

where $\boldsymbol{L}$ is the lower triangular matrix which is written below the $\boldsymbol{T}$

matrix in the condensed elimination method. Thus the first stage of the elimination is equivalent to a factorization of $\boldsymbol{A}$ into two triangular ices

$$\boldsymbol{A} = (\boldsymbol{I} + \boldsymbol{L})\boldsymbol{T} \tag{3.7.10}$$

and the array which is calculated includes all the elements of $\boldsymbol{L}$ and $\boldsymbol{T}$ which are not zero by definition.

This product form for $\boldsymbol{A}$ gives a simple proof of a result used earlier for, since it is clear that

$$|\boldsymbol{I} + \boldsymbol{L}| = 1 \tag{3.7.11}$$

the determinant

$$|\boldsymbol{A}| = |\boldsymbol{T}| \tag{3.7.12}$$

and, this $|\boldsymbol{T}|$ is the product of its diagonal elements, so that

$$|\boldsymbol{A}| = a_{11}b_{22}c_{33} \dots \tag{3.7.13}$$

3.8 Symmetric Matrices

The condensed elimination method can be applied without difficulty when the set of equations has a symmetric matrix. There is a more efficient method possible, however, which uses the symmetry of the matrix to reduce the labour. Symmetrical matrices occur so often in such physical applications as the theory of normal vibrations, molecular quantum mechanics and the normal equations in fitting by least squares, that it is worthwhile to have a special procedure.

The factorization of a matrix into the product of a lower triangular matrix and an upper triangular matrix is no longer unique if the diagonal elements of both matrices are independent variables. The product in 3.7 is made unique by choosing the diagonal elements of the lower matrix to be unity. For a symmetrical matrix a more useful restriction is that the diagonal elements of the two matrices should be equal. From this it can be proved that the two matrices are transposes of each other i.e.

$$\boldsymbol{A} = \tilde{\boldsymbol{S}}\boldsymbol{S} \tag{3.8.1}$$

where $\boldsymbol{S}$ is an upper triangular matrix. The method of calculating $\boldsymbol{S}$ is made apparent by equating elements on both sides of (1)

$$\begin{aligned} a_{11} &= s_{11}^2; & a_{1k} &= s_{11}s_{1k} \\ a_{22} &= s_{12}^2 + s_{22}^2; & a_{2k} &= s_{12}s_{1k} + s_{22}s_{2k}; \dots \end{aligned} \tag{3.8.2}$$

Thus, the diagonal elements involve square roots, which are always taken as positive,

$$\begin{aligned} s_{11} &= \sqrt{a_{11}} \\ s_{22} &= \sqrt{(a_{22} - s_{12}^2)}, \dots \end{aligned} \tag{3.8.3}$$

It can happen that a diagonal element is a pure imaginary but in that event all the off-diagonal elements are also imaginary and the equations are no more difficult to solve. The off-diagonal elements have formulae in the same form as for $\boldsymbol{L}$ in 3.2.8 and 3.7

$$\begin{aligned} s_{1k} &= a_{1k}/s_{11} \\ s_{2k} &= (a_{2k} - s_{12}s_{1k})/s_{22}\ , \ldots \end{aligned} \tag{3.8.4}$$

The numerical procedure is then the same as before for $\boldsymbol{L}$, except for the diagonal elements which are the square root of those in $\boldsymbol{T}$.

The primary advantage of this method is that only the one triangular matrix has to be calculated and recorded. The checking procedure used before is still applicable. An example which illustrates this modified method is given in Table 3.3. A secondary advantage of the method is that, for a fixed number of decimals, it gives more accurate solutions than the more general method. This happens because division by the square roots in (4) is less dependent on rounding-off error than division by the numbers themselves as in calculating $\boldsymbol{L}$.

TABLE 3.3

Solution of symmetric equations

$$\begin{aligned} 4a - 6b + 4c \quad &= 4 \\ -6a + 10b - 3c + 2d &= 13 \\ 4a - 3b + 14c + 5d &= 60 \\ 2b + 5c + 9d &= 55 \end{aligned}$$

2	−3	2	0	2
	1	3	2	19
		1	−1	−1
			2	8
1	2	3	4	

3.9 Other Elimination Methods

The condensed elimination method has many minor modifications. Some of these concern the layout of the array and are matters of convenience. One, which is of more theoretical interest, is equivalent to taking the upper triangular matrix as the one with the unit elements in its diagonal. This form of the method is described in many textbooks.

The elimination method can also be combined with the partitioning method described in chapter 2. This partitioning method involves the calculation of the reciprocals of a number of submatrices and so is usually slower than the direct elimination method. In some circumstances, however, it may become a profitable method. It may happen, for example, that the reciprocals required are easily found, e.g. triangular matrices or matrices equal to one another. The method is also needed when the number of variables becomes larger than it is possible to manipulate simultaneously.

All these methods have the common advantage of yielding the final result after a finite fixed number of operations. They also have in common the disadvantage that rounding-off error becomes larger and larger as the calculation proceeds. In contrast, there are iteration methods in which an approximate solution is steadily improved. The number of operations needed to obtain a solution of prescribed accuracy is not fixed and depends largely on the accuracy of the initial guessed solution. On the other hand, the final accuracy is not limited by rounding-off error and can always be increased.

3.10 An Iteration Method

One of the most useful of the iteration methods of solving simultaneous linear equations begins by dividing the matrix of the equations into two parts. To do this in an effective way, the equations have first to be rearranged as described in section 3.4 and then rescaled so that all the diagonal elements are unity. The matrix is then divided as

$$\boldsymbol{A} = \boldsymbol{I} - \boldsymbol{B} \tag{3.10.1}$$

and the original equations,

$$\boldsymbol{Ax} = \boldsymbol{v} \tag{3.10.2}$$

become

$$\boldsymbol{x} = \boldsymbol{Bx} + \boldsymbol{v} \tag{3.10.3}$$

where all the elements of $\boldsymbol{B}$ should now be small.

The solution of (2) is found by the iteration formula suggested by (3) viz.

$$\boldsymbol{x}_n = \boldsymbol{Bx}_{n-1} + \boldsymbol{v} \tag{3.10.4}$$

If $\boldsymbol{x}_0$ is taken as an approximate solution, (4) enables the sequence of vectors $\boldsymbol{x}_1, \boldsymbol{x}_2, \ldots$ to be generated rapidly. It can be shown that, if $\boldsymbol{B}$ is sufficiently small, this sequence of vectors will converge to the correct solution no matter what $\boldsymbol{x}_0$ is used. If no better estimate is available, it is possible to take $\boldsymbol{x}_0 = \boldsymbol{v}$. In practice the convergence of the sequence is often slow and it is better to use the first few vectors to extrapolate and estimate the limiting vector and then use this as the $\boldsymbol{x}_0$ for a new sequence. This extrapolation can be carried out systematically and accurately on a computer but, in hand computation, it is easier to note that the differences between corresponding components of successive vectors are often approximately in geometric progression and so can be extrapolated approximately but rapidly. (See section 4.5.)

The principal advantage in this method, as in most iteration methods, is the easy control over accuracy which it provides. At the beginning of the calculation no more decimal places need be retained than can reasonably be expected to be accurate. This reduces quite considerably the labour of a hand calculation. As the solution becomes more accurate the number of decimals can be steadily increased. Furthermore, successive iterations serve to check each other so that no independent check is necessary. Occasional numerical mistakes, provided they are not systematic, may delay the convergence but they will not prevent the true solution from being obtained eventually.

In order to indicate more precisely the meaning of the condition that $\boldsymbol{B}$ should be small it is interesting to quote one theorem. This states that, if $\boldsymbol{B}$ satisfies the inequalities

$$\sum_i |B_{ik}| < 1, \qquad \text{for all } k$$

then the iteration process converges. Other less stringent conditions will be given later.

An example of this method is illustrated in Table 3.4. The initial $\boldsymbol{x}_0$ is rather poor and there are considerable changes in the $\boldsymbol{x}_i$. From the first four vectors a new $\boldsymbol{x}_0$ is found by extrapolation and further interations indicate how accurate it is.

TABLE 3.4

Iteration solution of linear equations

$$\begin{aligned} 6a + 3b - 2c + d &= 5 \\ -a + 8b + 2c - 3d &= 24 \\ b + 2c + d &= 7 \\ a + 2b - c + 4d &= -2 \end{aligned}$$

$\boldsymbol{B}$	$\boldsymbol{x}_0 = \boldsymbol{v}$	$\boldsymbol{x}_1$	$\boldsymbol{x}_2$	$\boldsymbol{x}_3$	$\boldsymbol{x}_4$	$\boldsymbol{x}_5$	$\boldsymbol{x}_6$
$\begin{pmatrix} 0 & -\frac{1}{2} & \frac{1}{3} & -\frac{1}{6} \\ \frac{1}{8} & 0 & -\frac{1}{4} & \frac{3}{8} \\ 0 & -\frac{1}{2} & 0 & -\frac{1}{2} \\ -\frac{1}{4} & -\frac{1}{2} & \frac{1}{4} & 0 \end{pmatrix}$	·833 3·000 3·500 −0·500	·583 2·042 2·250 −1·333	·784 2·011 3·145 −1·105	1·159 1·898 3·046 −0·916	1·052 2·039 3·009 −0·977	0·979 2·013 2·969 −1·031	0·988 1·993 3·009 −1·010

One particularly useful application of this method is in improving a solution which is already a good approximation. The method of using the residuals given in section 3.4 is actually this iteration method in a slightly different form.

3.11 Orthonormalization of a Set of Vectors

In different contexts the problem often arises of finding, from a set of non-orthogonal vectors, a set which will span the same space and be orthonormal. There is a close similarity between this problem and that of solving linear equations, and the procedures discussed in section 3.8 provide a convenient solution.

The original set of r vectors, v_i, is in an n-dimensional space ($n \geqslant r$). Indices in this section will, in consequence, take values up to r whereas vectors and scalar products are in the n-dimensional space. Since the vectors are non-orthogonal the scalar products,

$$S_{ik} = v_i \cdot v_k \tag{3.11.1}$$

do not vanish and form an $r \times r$ matrix known as the overlap matrix. The problem is to construct a set of vectors a_i which are linear combinations of the v_i and have a unit overlap matrix

$$a_i \cdot a_k = \delta_{ik} \tag{3.11.2}$$

The method of solution is easily understood in geometrical terms. The first vector a_1 is taken in the same direction as v_1 but is

$$a_1 = v_1(S_{11})^{-\frac{1}{2}} \tag{3.11.3}$$

by normalization. The second vector v_2 along with a_1 defines a plane, but is not in a suitable direction because it is not orthogonal to a_1. If, however, its projection on to a_1 is subtracted, the result will be orthogonal and hence

$$a_2 = [v_2 - a_1(a_1 \cdot v_2)](S_{22} - S_{12}^2/S_{11})^{-\frac{1}{2}} \tag{3.11.4}$$

In general, v_k is made orthogonal to the previous a_i by subtracting all its projected parts on them and the result is normalized to give a_k. This is known as the Schmidt orthogonalization process and is convenient numerically if the mixed scalar products $a_i \cdot v_k$ are readily available. If these scalar products have first to be deduced from the S_{ik} it is not usually an efficient process.

The relation of this solution to the procedure in section 3.8 is made clear by a formal analysis of the solution. The equations, such as (4), which define the a_i can be written as

$$a_i B_{ij} = v_j \tag{3.11.5}$$

where B_{ij} is an upper triangular matrix of order r. From (1) and (2) it follows that

$$S_{ik} = B_{xi} B_{yk} a_x \cdot a_y = B_{xi} B_{xk} \tag{3.11.6}$$

so that the symmetrical matrix S_{ik} is the product of the triangular matrix and its transpose. The first stage of the procedure in 3.8 is, therefore, a practical method of deducing the matrix B_{ij} from the overlap matrix.

The procedure of section 3.8 can also be extended to enable a_i to be expressed in terms of v_j. The argument begins by considering a different problem viz. that of finding vectors w_k defined by

$$S_{ik} w_k = v_i \tag{3.11.7}$$

Equation (7) can also be written as

$$B_{xi} B_{xk} w_k = v_i \tag{3.11.8}$$

or, using (5), as the simultaneous equations

$$B_{xi} a_x = v_i \tag{3.11.9}$$

$$B_{xk} w_k = a_x \tag{3.11.10}$$

Now, according to the procedure of section 3.8, the first stage in the reduction of the equations (7) gives a triangular set which is (10). Thus, if an extra column, whose elements are the vectors v_i, is added to the right of S_{ik} and the elimination carried out the new vectors to the right of the triangular matrix will be the a_i.

The problem of finding an orthonormal set is not one which has a unique solution. This is obvious since a set of orthonormal vectors can be rotated rigidly through any angle and will still span the space. The Schmidt process selects solutions which can be obtained using a triangular matrix. Other processes may select solutions of a different type.

EXERCISES

1. Solve, using the condensed elimination method without rearrangement,

$$\begin{aligned} 2a + b + 3c + 4d &= -3 \\ 2a + 2b - c + d &= 6 \\ 4a + 3b + 3c + 2d &= 9 \\ 2a + 3b + 4c + 3d &= 5 \end{aligned} \qquad \begin{aligned} 3x + 2y + z - w &= 3 \\ -3x - y + 2z + w &= 2 \\ 6x + y + 7z - 3w &= 2 \\ 9x - y - 2z + 2w &= 5 \end{aligned}$$

2. Solve, using the square root method,

$$\begin{aligned} 4l + 2s + 6f &= 12 \\ 2l + 2s + d + f &= 1 \\ s + 5d - 4f &= -15 \\ 6l + s - 4d + 15f &= 34 \end{aligned} \qquad \begin{aligned} 16p + 8v + 4r - 4t &= 8 \\ 8p + 5v + 2r - 5t &= -1 \\ 4p + 2v + 5r - t &= 16 \\ -4p - 5v + r + 10t &= 19 \end{aligned}$$

3. Rearrange and solve by iteration

$$\begin{aligned} 2m - 30a + 8t - s &= 24 \\ 4m + 20a + 2t &= 14 \\ -2m + 10a + 3t + 6s &= 5 \\ -m + 40a + 2t + s &= -2 \end{aligned}$$

takes a long time!

4. Factorize in the form $\tilde{S}S$, where S is upper triangular, the matrix

$$\begin{pmatrix} 9 & 12 & 18 \\ 12 & 20 & 18 \\ 18 & 18 & 41 \end{pmatrix}$$

and form the product $S\tilde{S}$.

5. Find the rank of the matrix

$$\begin{pmatrix} 2 & 3 & -1 & 6 \\ 1 & -1 & 2 & 5\sqrt{2} \\ 1 & 1 & -3 & -11 \\ 1 & -1 & 3 & 12 \end{pmatrix}$$

working (a) to 2 decimals, (b) to higher accuracy.

6. Show how the iteration formula (3.10.4) provides a justification for the residual method 3.4.

7. Show that the series inversion formula of 2.6 gives the same result as the iteration formula for (3.10.3) when $\boldsymbol{x}_0 = \boldsymbol{v}$.

8. Prove that a Hermitian matrix can be factorized in the form $\boldsymbol{T}^\dagger\boldsymbol{T}$, where $\boldsymbol{T}$ is upper triangular.

9. Prove that the direct product of two vectors is a matrix of rank one. Is the converse true?

10. Vectors, u, v, w, have the overlap matrix

$$\begin{pmatrix} 4 & -4 & 6 \\ -4 & 5 & -4 \\ 6 & -4 & 22 \end{pmatrix}$$

I does the trick...

Find an orthonormal set spanning the same space.

11. Find the rank of the matrices

$$\begin{pmatrix} 1 & -2 & -1 \\ 2 & -4 & -2 \\ -1 & 2 & 1 \end{pmatrix}; \quad \begin{pmatrix} 2 & -1 & 1 \\ 1 & 1 & 2 \\ -1 & 2 & 1 \end{pmatrix}; \quad \begin{pmatrix} 3 & 1 & -1 \\ -1 & 1 & 2 \\ -2 & 2 & 1 \end{pmatrix}$$

CHAPTER 4

EIGENVALUES AND EIGENVECTORS

4.1 Basic Definitions

An eigenvalue of a matrix $\boldsymbol{A}$, of order n, is defined as a number λ (which may be complex even when all the elements of $\boldsymbol{A}$ are real) which satisfies the equation

$$\boldsymbol{A}\boldsymbol{x} = \lambda\boldsymbol{x} \tag{4.1.1}$$

for some non-zero vector $\boldsymbol{x}$. This vector is defined to be the corresponding eigenvector. The importance of a study of eigenvalues and eigenvectors to a chemist is threefold. In the first place they are fundamental quantities of a matrix and essential to any deeper understanding of a matrix property or problem. Secondly, the theory of eigenproperties, of which this is the simplest instance, has influenced the development of quantum mechanics to such an extent that it has become a necessary part of the mathematical background to modern chemistry and physics. Finally, equations such as (1) occur so frequently in practical applications, both of quantum mechanics and of other theories, that it is of importance to know several practicable methods of solving them and to understand their relative merits.

By inserting the unit matrix $\boldsymbol{I}$ the eigenvector equations take the form

$$(\boldsymbol{A} - \lambda\boldsymbol{I})\boldsymbol{x} = 0 \tag{4.1.2}$$

which shows them to be a set of homogeneous linear equations. For a square matrix $\boldsymbol{A}$ and arbitrary λ these equations are usually inconsistent and have only the trivial solution

$$\boldsymbol{x} = 0 \tag{4.1.3}$$

(c.f. 3.6.1). To have a non-zero solution the equations (2) have to satisfy the condition

$$|\boldsymbol{A} - \lambda\boldsymbol{I}| = 0 \tag{4.1.4}$$

This is an equation of the nth degree to determine λ and is known as the eigenvalue equation or the secular determinantal equation. For each value of λ satisfying (4) there will be a corresponding eigenvector found by solving (2).

The solution of the equations

$$\tilde{\boldsymbol{x}}\boldsymbol{A} = \lambda\tilde{\boldsymbol{x}} \tag{4.1.5}$$

is very similar. The vectors $\tilde{\boldsymbol{x}}$ may be called eigenrows to distinguish them from the eigencolumns above. The eigenvalue equation is still (4) so that to each eigenvalue λ there is a corresponding eigenrow and an eigencolumn.

These equations have a direct geometrical significance. In general the effect of multiplying a matrix into a vector is to give a vector in some other direction. The eigenvectors are those particular vectors whose directions are not changed by the multiplication and the eigenvalue represents the magnifying effect of the matrix in these directions.

4.2 Orthogonality Relations

There are a number of relations both between the eigenvectors of a matrix and between the eigenvectors of related matrices which are of theoretical importance and also assist in determining these vectors in practice. The first concerns the eigenrows and eigencolumns of a single matrix $\boldsymbol{A}$.

THEOREM A. Eigenrows are orthogonal to eigencolumns belonging to different eigenvalues.

The proof of this is immediate for, if the eigencolumn $\boldsymbol{x}$ satisfies

$$\boldsymbol{A}\boldsymbol{x} = \lambda\boldsymbol{x} \tag{4.2.1}$$

and the eigenrow $\tilde{\boldsymbol{y}}$

$$\tilde{\boldsymbol{y}}\boldsymbol{A} = \mu\tilde{\boldsymbol{y}} \tag{4.2.2}$$

then, by multiplying in two ways,

$$\tilde{\boldsymbol{y}}\boldsymbol{A}\boldsymbol{x} = \lambda\tilde{\boldsymbol{y}}\boldsymbol{x} = \mu\tilde{\boldsymbol{y}}\boldsymbol{x} \tag{4.2.3}$$

so that

$$(\lambda - \mu)\tilde{\boldsymbol{y}}\boldsymbol{x} = 0 \tag{4.2.4}$$

Thus, for $\lambda \neq \mu$, the orthogonality relation

$$\tilde{\boldsymbol{y}}\boldsymbol{x} = 0 \tag{4.2.5}$$

must hold.

Other relationships can be established by using the operations defined in 2.4. Thus, by taking the transpose of (2),

$$\tilde{\boldsymbol{A}}\boldsymbol{y} = \mu\boldsymbol{y} \tag{4.2.6}$$

so that an eigenrow of $\boldsymbol{A}$ is the transpose of an eigencolumn of $\tilde{\boldsymbol{A}}$ with the same eigenvalue. A corollary of this is that the eigenrows of a symmetrical matrix are the transposes of its eigencolumns and hence that the eigencolumns belonging to different eigenvalues are orthogonal to each other. Again, taking the complex conjugate of (1),

$$\boldsymbol{A}^*\boldsymbol{x}^* = \lambda^*\boldsymbol{x}^* \tag{4.2.7}$$

and the complex conjugate matrix has eigenvalues and eigencolumns which are the complex conjugates of those of $\boldsymbol{A}$. When $\boldsymbol{A}$ is real, it follows that the eigenvalues and eigenvectors are either real or can be associated in pairs which are complex conjugates of one another.

When $\boldsymbol{A}$ is a Hermitian matrix the Hermitian conjugate of (1) is

$$\boldsymbol{x}^\dagger\boldsymbol{A} = \lambda^*\boldsymbol{x}^\dagger \tag{4.2.8}$$

so that its eigenrows are the Hermitian conjugate of its eigencolumns. Theorem A also shows that

$$(\lambda - \lambda^*)\boldsymbol{x}^\dagger\boldsymbol{x} = 0 \tag{4.2.9}$$

but the Hermitian scalar product $\boldsymbol{x}^\dagger\boldsymbol{x}$ is always the sum of squares and so always positive therefore

$$\lambda = \lambda^* \tag{4.2.10}$$

If $\boldsymbol{y}$ is an eigencolumn with an eigenvalue $\mu \neq \lambda$ then Theorem A implies also that

$$\boldsymbol{y}^\dagger\boldsymbol{x} = 0 \tag{4.2.11}$$

It is convenient to summarize these results in a theorem.

THEOREM B. The eigenvalues of a Hermitian matrix are all real. Eigenrows are the Hermitian conjugates of eigencolumns. Eigencolumns belonging to different eigenvalues are orthogonal in the Hermitian sense.

Theorems similar in type to Theorem B can be proved for the other special types of matrix. Some of these are given in the exercises.

4.3 Diagonalization of a Matrix

The eigenvector equations for a matrix $\boldsymbol{A}$, which has n distinct eigenvalues, are

$$\boldsymbol{A}\boldsymbol{x}_i = \lambda_i\boldsymbol{x}_i\,, \qquad i = 1, 2, \ldots, n \tag{4.3.1}$$

These can be written in a more compact form by constructing a matrix $\boldsymbol{X}$ whose columns are the eigencolumns

$$\boldsymbol{X} = (\boldsymbol{x}_1 \boldsymbol{x}_2 \dots \boldsymbol{x}_n) \qquad (4.3.2)$$

The equations now become

$$\boldsymbol{AX} = \boldsymbol{X}\Lambda \qquad (4.3.3)$$

where Λ is a matrix whose off-diagonal elements are all zero and which is defined by its diagonal elements in the notation

$$\Lambda = \ulcorner \lambda_1 \lambda_2 \dots \lambda_n \lrcorner \qquad (4.3.4)$$

Similarly the eigenrows $\tilde{\boldsymbol{y}}_i$ can be combined together as the rows of a matrix $\tilde{\boldsymbol{Y}}$ i.e.

$$\boldsymbol{Y} = (\boldsymbol{y}_1 \boldsymbol{y}_2 \dots \boldsymbol{y}_n) \qquad (4.3.5)$$

If the numbering of the eigenrows and eigenvalues corresponds, then the eigenrow equations are

$$\tilde{\boldsymbol{Y}}\boldsymbol{A} = \Lambda \tilde{\boldsymbol{Y}} \qquad (4.3.6)$$

Theorem A of section 4.2 implies that

$$\tilde{\boldsymbol{y}}_i \boldsymbol{x}_j = 0 \,, \qquad i \neq j \qquad (4.3.7)$$

since all the eigenvalues are distinct. The normalization of the eigenvectors has not yet been fixed so it is convenient now to use it to arrange that

$$\tilde{\boldsymbol{y}}_i \boldsymbol{x}_i = 1 \qquad (4.3.8)$$

The equations (7) and (8) reduce, therefore, to the simpler matrix relation

$$\tilde{\boldsymbol{Y}}\boldsymbol{X} = \boldsymbol{I} \qquad (4.3.9)$$

Equations (9) and either (3) or (6) now imply that

$$\boldsymbol{X}^{-1}\boldsymbol{AX} = \tilde{\boldsymbol{Y}}\boldsymbol{AX} = \Lambda \qquad (4.3.10)$$

Thus the matrix $\boldsymbol{A}$ can be simplified into a diagonal matrix by multiplication by the matrix $\boldsymbol{X}$ and its inverse. This is the process known as diagonalization.

When a matrix has repeated eigenvalues the argument above, and that in theorem A, fails and a more elaborate theory is required. One result in this theory, which is of importance here, is that any normal matrix, i.e. one for which

$$\boldsymbol{A}^\dagger \boldsymbol{A} = \boldsymbol{A}\boldsymbol{A}^\dagger \qquad (4.3.11)$$

has n eigenvectors and can be reduced to diagonal form. The great majority of the matrices used in physics and chemistry are normal but some of the exceptions are important.

A second way of considering this process of diagonalization is in terms of projection operators. From (3) and (6) the matrix can be written

$$\boldsymbol{A} = \boldsymbol{X}\Lambda\tilde{\boldsymbol{Y}} \tag{4.3.12}$$

or as

$$\boldsymbol{A} = \sum_i \lambda_i(\boldsymbol{x}_i\tilde{\boldsymbol{y}}_i) \equiv \sum_i \lambda_i \boldsymbol{P}_i \tag{4.3.13}$$

Each term in this sum contains a direct product of an eigencolumn and an eigenrow. Such a direct product is a projection operator of the type discussed in section 2.8 and projects any vector, on which it acts, on to the eigenvector. Furthermore, from the orthogonality relations, two different projection operators annihilate each other since

$$\boldsymbol{P}_i\boldsymbol{P}_k = \boldsymbol{x}_i\tilde{\boldsymbol{y}}_i\boldsymbol{x}_k\tilde{\boldsymbol{y}}_k = \boldsymbol{x}_i(\tilde{\boldsymbol{y}}_i\boldsymbol{x}_k)\tilde{\boldsymbol{y}}_k = 0 \qquad (i \neq k)\,. \tag{4.3.14}$$

These relations are summarized in the equation

$$\boldsymbol{P}_i\boldsymbol{P}_k = \delta_{ik}\boldsymbol{P}_k \tag{4.3.15}$$

The square of a matrix has the same eigenvectors as the matrix itself but its eigenvalues are the squares. This result follows immediately from the eigenvector equation for, if

$$\boldsymbol{A}\boldsymbol{x}_i = \lambda_i\boldsymbol{x}_i \tag{4.3.16}$$

then

$$\boldsymbol{A}^2\boldsymbol{x}_i = \lambda_i\boldsymbol{A}\boldsymbol{x}_i = \lambda_i^2\boldsymbol{x}_i \tag{4.3.17}$$

Similarly, for any integral power of the matrix, the eigenvectors are unaltered but the eigenvalues are the same power of the original eigenvalues. The same argument applies for any polynomial in $\boldsymbol{A}$ and by further argument it can be shown generally that for any function

$$f(\boldsymbol{A})\boldsymbol{x}_i = f(\lambda_i)\boldsymbol{x}_i \tag{4.3.18}$$

For a normal matrix or a matrix whose eigenvalues are distinct this result can be used to calculate functions of a matrix for

$$f(\boldsymbol{A}) = \sum_i f(\lambda_i)\boldsymbol{P}_i \tag{4.3.19}$$

Equation (19) has considerable practical value, e.g. in constructing matrices such as

$$\boldsymbol{A}^{\frac{1}{2}} = \sum_i \lambda_i^{\frac{1}{2}}\boldsymbol{P}_i \tag{4.3.20}$$

and is also theoretically important, e.g. in reducing the problem of convergence of a matrix series to that of the convergence of the corresponding numerical series for each of the eigenvalues.

Another important relation which follows from the expansion of a matrix in terms of projection operators is the trace rule. This rule states that the trace of a matrix, which is the sum of its diagonal elements, is equal to the sum of its eigenvalues. Since

$$\boldsymbol{A} = \sum_i \lambda_i(\boldsymbol{x}_i\tilde{\boldsymbol{y}}_i) \tag{4.3.21}$$

its trace involves the trace of the direct product $\boldsymbol{x}_i\tilde{\boldsymbol{y}}_i$ which is just the scalar product $\tilde{\boldsymbol{y}}_i\boldsymbol{x}_i$ and this is unity by normalization. Thus,

$$\operatorname{Tr} \boldsymbol{A} = \sum_k a_{kk} = \sum_i \lambda_i \operatorname{Tr} (\boldsymbol{x}_i\tilde{\boldsymbol{y}}_i) = \sum_i \lambda_i \tag{4.3.22}$$

which is the result required. A simple extension of this result is that

$$\operatorname{Tr} [f(\boldsymbol{A})] = \sum_i f(\lambda_i) \tag{4.3.23}$$

4.4 Some Simple Examples

The theorems discussed in previous sections are sufficient to enable the eigenvalues and eigenvectors of some simple matrices to be calculated. It is advantageous to illustrate the basic concepts now, using some simple matrices, before developing more powerful and elaborate techniques.

Real symmetrical matrices occur so frequently that the first example must be of this type. The matrix chosen is

$$\boldsymbol{A} = \begin{pmatrix} 5 & 1 & -1 \\ 1 & 3 & -1 \\ -1 & -1 & 3 \end{pmatrix} \tag{4.4.1}$$

The eigenvalue equation is

$$|\boldsymbol{A} - \lambda\boldsymbol{I}| \equiv \begin{vmatrix} 5-\lambda & 1 & -1 \\ 1 & 3-\lambda & -1 \\ -1 & -1 & 3-\lambda \end{vmatrix} = 0 \tag{4.4.2}$$

On multiplication and simplification this becomes

$$(2 - \lambda)(3 - \lambda)(6 - \lambda) = 0 \tag{4.4.3}$$

so that the eigenvalues are 2, 3, 6. The trace rule gives a check on these values. For $\lambda = 2$ the eigenvector equations are

$$\begin{aligned} 3x + y - z &= 0 \\ x + y - z &= 0 \\ -x - y + z &= 0 \end{aligned} \tag{4.4.4}$$

and these give the solutions

$$x = 0\,; \qquad y = z \tag{4.4.5}$$

so that the eigenvector is

$$(0, 1, 1) \tag{4.4.6}$$

or, when normalized so that the length is unity,

$$\tilde{\boldsymbol{x}}_1 = \sqrt{\tfrac{1}{2}}(0, 1, 1) \tag{4.4.7}$$

Similarly, for $\lambda = 3$, the eigenvector equations are

$$\begin{aligned} 2x + y - z &= 0 \\ x \qquad - z &= 0 \\ x + y \qquad &= 0 \end{aligned} \tag{4.4.8}$$

so that, in normalized form,

$$\tilde{\boldsymbol{x}}_2 = \sqrt{\tfrac{1}{3}}(1, -1, 1) \tag{4.4.9}$$

Finally, when $\lambda = 6$, the eigenvector is

$$\tilde{\boldsymbol{x}}_3 = \sqrt{\tfrac{1}{6}}(2, 1, -1) \tag{4.4.10}$$

The matrix of eigencolumns is therefore

$$\boldsymbol{X} = \begin{pmatrix} 0 & \sqrt{\frac{1}{3}} & 2\sqrt{\frac{1}{6}} \\ \sqrt{\frac{1}{2}} & -\sqrt{\frac{1}{3}} & \sqrt{\frac{1}{6}} \\ \sqrt{\frac{1}{2}} & \sqrt{\frac{1}{3}} & -\sqrt{\frac{1}{6}} \end{pmatrix} \tag{4.4.11}$$

and the matrix of eigenrows is its transpose. The orthogonality relations show that $\boldsymbol{X}$ is an orthogonal matrix, i.e.

$$\tilde{\boldsymbol{X}}\boldsymbol{X} = \begin{pmatrix} 0 & \sqrt{\frac{1}{2}} & \sqrt{\frac{1}{2}} \\ \sqrt{\frac{1}{3}} & -\sqrt{\frac{1}{3}} & \sqrt{\frac{1}{3}} \\ 2\sqrt{\frac{1}{6}} & \sqrt{\frac{1}{6}} & -\sqrt{\frac{1}{6}} \end{pmatrix} \begin{pmatrix} 0 & \sqrt{\frac{1}{3}} & 2\sqrt{\frac{1}{6}} \\ \sqrt{\frac{1}{2}} & -\sqrt{\frac{1}{3}} & \sqrt{\frac{1}{6}} \\ \sqrt{\frac{1}{2}} & \sqrt{\frac{1}{3}} & -\sqrt{\frac{1}{6}} \end{pmatrix} = \begin{pmatrix} 1 & 0 & 0 \\ 0 & 1 & 0 \\ 0 & 0 & 1 \end{pmatrix} \tag{4.4.12}$$

The diagonalization of $\boldsymbol{A}$ is then shown by

$$\begin{pmatrix} 0 & \sqrt{\frac{1}{2}} & \sqrt{\frac{1}{2}} \\ \sqrt{\frac{1}{3}} & -\sqrt{\frac{1}{3}} & \sqrt{\frac{1}{3}} \\ 2\sqrt{\frac{1}{6}} & \sqrt{\frac{1}{6}} & -\sqrt{\frac{1}{6}} \end{pmatrix} \begin{pmatrix} 5 & 1 & -1 \\ 1 & 3 & -1 \\ -1 & -1 & 3 \end{pmatrix} \begin{pmatrix} 0 & \sqrt{\frac{1}{3}} & 2\sqrt{\frac{1}{6}} \\ \sqrt{\frac{1}{2}} & -\sqrt{\frac{1}{3}} & \sqrt{\frac{1}{6}} \\ \sqrt{\frac{1}{2}} & \sqrt{\frac{1}{3}} & -\sqrt{\frac{1}{6}} \end{pmatrix}$$

$$= \begin{pmatrix} 2 & 0 & 0 \\ 0 & 3 & 0 \\ 0 & 0 & 6 \end{pmatrix} \tag{4.4.13}$$

The first projection operator is

$$\boldsymbol{x}_1\tilde{\boldsymbol{x}}_1 = \tfrac{1}{2}\begin{pmatrix} 0 \\ 1 \\ 1 \end{pmatrix}\begin{pmatrix} 0 & 1 & 1 \end{pmatrix} = \tfrac{1}{2}\begin{pmatrix} 0 & 0 & 0 \\ 0 & 1 & 1 \\ 0 & 1 & 1 \end{pmatrix} = \begin{pmatrix} 0 & 0 & 0 \\ 0 & \frac{1}{2} & \frac{1}{2} \\ 0 & \frac{1}{2} & \frac{1}{2} \end{pmatrix} \tag{4.4.14}$$

the second is

$$\boldsymbol{x}_2\tilde{\boldsymbol{x}}_2 = \tfrac{1}{3}\begin{pmatrix}1\\-1\\1\end{pmatrix}(1 \quad -1 \quad 1) = \begin{pmatrix}\frac{1}{3} & -\frac{1}{3} & \frac{1}{3}\\ -\frac{1}{3} & \frac{1}{3} & -\frac{1}{3}\\ \frac{1}{3} & -\frac{1}{3} & \frac{1}{3}\end{pmatrix} \tag{4.4.15}$$

while the third is

$$\boldsymbol{x}_3\tilde{\boldsymbol{x}}_3 = \tfrac{1}{6}\begin{pmatrix}2\\1\\-1\end{pmatrix}(2 \quad 1 \quad -1) = \begin{pmatrix}\frac{2}{3} & \frac{1}{3} & -\frac{1}{3}\\ \frac{1}{3} & \frac{1}{6} & -\frac{1}{6}\\ -\frac{1}{3} & -\frac{1}{6} & \frac{1}{6}\end{pmatrix} \tag{4.4.16}$$

The projection operator expansion of the matrix is then

$$\begin{pmatrix}5 & 1 & -1\\ 1 & 3 & -1\\ -1 & -1 & 3\end{pmatrix} = 2\begin{pmatrix}0 & 0 & 0\\ 0 & \frac{1}{2} & \frac{1}{2}\\ 0 & \frac{1}{2} & \frac{1}{2}\end{pmatrix} + 3\begin{pmatrix}\frac{1}{3} & -\frac{1}{3} & \frac{1}{3}\\ -\frac{1}{3} & \frac{1}{3} & -\frac{1}{3}\\ \frac{1}{3} & -\frac{1}{3} & \frac{1}{3}\end{pmatrix} + 6\begin{pmatrix}\frac{2}{3} & \frac{1}{3} & -\frac{1}{3}\\ \frac{1}{3} & \frac{1}{6} & -\frac{1}{6}\\ -\frac{1}{3} & -\frac{1}{6} & \frac{1}{6}\end{pmatrix} \tag{4.4.17}$$

and the sum of the projection operators is the unit matrix.

A second example illustrates the more general form of the matrix, which has no symmetry properties. The matrix is

$$\boldsymbol{A} = \begin{pmatrix}7 & 29 & -18\\ 5 & 3 & 10\\ -2 & 8 & 12\end{pmatrix} \tag{4.4.18}$$

and has the eigenvalue equation

$$\begin{vmatrix}7-\lambda & 29 & -18\\ 5 & 3-\lambda & 10\\ -2 & 8 & 12-\lambda\end{vmatrix} = 0 \tag{4.4.19}$$

which can be simplified into

$$-3456 + 120\lambda + 22\lambda^2 - \lambda^3 = -(16-\lambda)(18-\lambda)(12+\lambda) = 0 \tag{4.4.20}$$

so that the eigenvalues are 16, 18, -12. The eigencolumn corresponding to $\lambda = 16$ satisfies

$$\begin{aligned}-9x + 29y - 18z &= 0\\ 5x - 13y + 10z &= 0\\ -2x + 8y - 4z &= 0\end{aligned} \tag{4.4.21}$$

and so is

$$\tilde{\boldsymbol{x}}_1 = (2, 0, -1) \tag{4.4.22}$$

while the eigenrow satisfies

$$\begin{aligned} -9x + 5y - 2z &= 0 \\ 29x - 13y + 8z &= 0 \\ -18x + 10y - 4z &= 0 \end{aligned} \tag{4.4.23}$$

and is

$$\tilde{\boldsymbol{y}}_1 = (1, 1, -2) \tag{4.4.24}$$

or, if the scalar product of the two is to be unity,

$$\tilde{\boldsymbol{y}}_1 = (\tfrac{1}{4}, \tfrac{1}{4}, -\tfrac{1}{2}) \tag{4.4.25}$$

Similarly the eigenvalue 18 corresponds to the eigenvectors

$$\tilde{\boldsymbol{x}}_2 = (1, 1, 1) \tag{4.4.26}$$

$$\tilde{\boldsymbol{y}}_2 = (\tfrac{1}{6}, \tfrac{1}{2}, \tfrac{1}{3}) \tag{4.4.27}$$

while, for $\lambda = -12$,

$$\tilde{\boldsymbol{x}}_3 = (4, -2, 1) \tag{4.4.28}$$

$$\tilde{\boldsymbol{y}}_3 = (\tfrac{1}{12}, -\tfrac{1}{4}, \tfrac{1}{6}) \tag{4.4.29}$$

The eigencolumns are collected into the matrix

$$\boldsymbol{X} = \begin{pmatrix} 2 & 1 & 4 \\ 0 & 1 & -2 \\ 1 & 1 & 1 \end{pmatrix} \tag{4.4.30}$$

and the eigencolumns into

$$\boldsymbol{Y} = \begin{pmatrix} \frac{1}{4} & \frac{1}{4} & -\frac{1}{2} \\ \frac{1}{6} & \frac{1}{2} & \frac{1}{3} \\ \frac{1}{12} & -\frac{1}{4} & \frac{1}{6} \end{pmatrix} \tag{4.4.31}$$

The orthogonality relations between these vectors are then summarized as

$$\tilde{\boldsymbol{Y}}\boldsymbol{X} = \boldsymbol{I} \tag{4.4.32}$$

and this is readily verified. Another way of expressing these relations is that the $\boldsymbol{y}_i$ are reciprocal vectors to the $\boldsymbol{x}_i$ in the sense defined in 1.8. The projection operator expansion for the matrix is

$$\begin{pmatrix} 7 & 29 & -18 \\ 5 & 3 & 10 \\ -2 & 8 & 12 \end{pmatrix} = 16 \begin{pmatrix} \frac{1}{2} & \frac{1}{2} & -1 \\ 0 & 0 & 0 \\ -\frac{1}{4} & -\frac{1}{4} & \frac{1}{2} \end{pmatrix} + 18 \begin{pmatrix} \frac{1}{6} & \frac{1}{2} & \frac{1}{3} \\ \frac{1}{6} & \frac{1}{2} & \frac{1}{3} \\ \frac{1}{6} & \frac{1}{2} & \frac{1}{6} \end{pmatrix} - 12 \begin{pmatrix} \frac{1}{3} & -1 & \frac{2}{3} \\ -\frac{1}{6} & \frac{1}{2} & -\frac{1}{3} \\ \frac{1}{12} & -\frac{1}{4} & \frac{1}{6} \end{pmatrix} \tag{4.4.33}$$

While these examples are typical of the form of result usually obtained, they are exceptional in that the eigenvalues are integers and the eigenvectors have fractional components. These features simplified the calculation very considerably at various points. The most significant of these is that the eigenvalue equation could be reduced to a polynomial equation and factorized very simply. For more general matrices the most efficient methods of finding the eigenvalues and eigenvectors do not involve deducing or solving this polynomial equation.

4.5 The Power Method

The power method is an easily applied iteration method of calculating the matrix eigenvalue which is numerically largest, together with its eigenvector. Since it is an iteration method it has the usual advantages of being self-checking, of having a simple basic operation, and of preventing the accumulation of rounding-off error. On the other hand, it has to be elaborated before it can be used for other eigenvalues and it becomes considerably less efficient if a large number of eigenvalues and eigenvectors has to be found.

The power method is simpler to describe and understand when the matrix has one real eigenvalue whose modulus is larger than that of any other eigenvalue, and this restriction will be imposed temporarily. The majority of matrices used in practical problems will satisfy this restriction. This largest eigenvalue will be labelled λ_1 and the one next largest in modulus, λ_2. If the matrix is normal or has its n eigenvalues distinct, then its n eigenvectors will span the n-dimensional space and any arbitrary vector $\boldsymbol{v}$ can be expressed in terms of them (see 23, p. 86) viz.

$$\boldsymbol{v} = v_1\boldsymbol{x}_1 + v_2\boldsymbol{x}_2 + \dots + v_n\boldsymbol{x}_n \tag{4.5.1}$$

If these conditions are not satisfied the eigenvectors have to be supplemented with some other vectors to span the space but this does not change the essential features of the argument. This vector $\boldsymbol{v}$ is now multiplied m times by the matrix $\boldsymbol{A}$ and becomes

$$\begin{aligned}\boldsymbol{v}_m \equiv \boldsymbol{A}^m\boldsymbol{v} &= v_1\lambda_1^m\boldsymbol{x}_1 + v_2\lambda_2^m\boldsymbol{x}_2 + \dots + v_n\lambda_n^m\boldsymbol{x}_n \\ &= \lambda_1^m\left[v_1\boldsymbol{x}_1 + v_2\left(\frac{\lambda_2}{\lambda_1}\right)^m\boldsymbol{x}_2 + \dots\right]\end{aligned} \tag{4.5.2}$$

Now, if $|\lambda_2| < |\lambda_1|$, the second and subsequent terms will become progressively smaller until, for sufficiently large m,

$$\boldsymbol{A}^m\boldsymbol{v} = \lambda_1^m v_1\boldsymbol{x}_1 \tag{4.5.3}$$

Thus the limiting form of $\boldsymbol{v}_m$ gives the eigenvector and the ratio of any pair of components of $\boldsymbol{v}_m$ and $\boldsymbol{v}_{m-1}$ gives the eigenvalue. In practice, it is convenient to normalize the vectors so that the largest component is made unity. The practical procedure is then to multiply the approximate eigenvector by $\boldsymbol{A}$, divide throughout by the largest component, compare with the starting vector, and repeat until the vector is consistent to the accuracy required. The approximate eigenvalue is then the largest component itself.

An example illustrating this method is shown in Table 4.1. The initial vector, of course, is arbitrary but the process will converge more rapidly if it is already a good approximation. The vector chosen here was suggested by the large diagonal element which governs the effect of the matrix on a vector.

TABLE 4.1

Power method for largest eigenvalue and eigenvector

$\boldsymbol{A}$				$\boldsymbol{v}_0$	$\boldsymbol{v}_1$	$\boldsymbol{y}_1$	$\boldsymbol{Ay}_1$	$\boldsymbol{y}_2$	$\boldsymbol{Ay}_2$	$\boldsymbol{y}_3$	$\boldsymbol{Ay}_3$	$\boldsymbol{y}_4$
5	1	2	1	1	5	1	6·6	1	6·31	1	6·40	1
2	−1	0	2	0	2	·4	1·6	·24	1·82	·29	1·69	·26
3	0	1	−2	0	3	·6	3·6	·55	3·49	·55	3·57	·56
0	2	−1	1	0	0	0	0·2	·03	−0·04	−·01	0·02	·00

$\bar{\boldsymbol{y}}_0$	$\boldsymbol{A}\bar{\boldsymbol{y}}_0$	$\bar{\boldsymbol{y}}_1$	$\boldsymbol{A}\bar{\boldsymbol{y}}_1$	$\bar{\boldsymbol{y}}_2$
1	6·389	1	6·386	1
·273	1·727	·270	1·726	·2703
·558	3·558	·558	3·561	·5576
·000	−0·012	−·002	−0·019	−·0030

It is comparatively easy to relax some of the restrictions on the matrix imposed above. Thus, if λ_1 is degenerate, the method need not be changed but it gives only one eigenvector. The other eigenvectors can be found by solving the eigenvector equations. Again, if λ_2 is approximately $-\lambda_1$, it is easy to show that the vectors will oscillate instead of converging. The simplest way of overcoming this difficulty is to replace $\boldsymbol{A}$ by

$$\boldsymbol{B} = \boldsymbol{A} + k\boldsymbol{I} \tag{4.5.4}$$

where k is a small positive constant. This matrix has the same eigenvectors but its eigenvalues are larger than those of $\boldsymbol{A}$ by k so that the degeneracy of modulus is removed. Sometimes the dominant eigenvalue λ_1 is complex and a more elaborate analysis, which is given in many textbooks, is needed. This eventuality can be recognized by an oscillation in signs of each component of the $\boldsymbol{v}_m$.

The practical difficulty in applying this method is that the convergence is often very slow. This can be understood and overcome by using a more detailed analysis. The ith component of $\boldsymbol{v}_m$ is just $\tilde{\boldsymbol{e}}_i\boldsymbol{v}_m$ and so, using (2),

$$\tilde{\boldsymbol{e}}_i\boldsymbol{v}_m = \lambda_1^m v_1\tilde{\boldsymbol{e}}_i\boldsymbol{x}_1[1 + (\lambda_2/\lambda_1)^m v_2\tilde{\boldsymbol{e}}_i\boldsymbol{x}_2/v_1\tilde{\boldsymbol{e}}_i\boldsymbol{x}_1 + \dots] \tag{4.5.5}$$

The eigenvalue is estimated from the ratio

$$r_m = \tilde{\boldsymbol{e}}_i\boldsymbol{v}_{m+1}/\tilde{\boldsymbol{e}}_i\boldsymbol{v}_m = \lambda_1[1 + (\lambda_2/\lambda_1)^m K + \dots] \tag{4.5.6}$$

where

$$K = -(1 - \lambda_2/\lambda_1)v_2\tilde{\boldsymbol{e}}_i\boldsymbol{x}_2/v_1\tilde{\boldsymbol{e}}_i\boldsymbol{x}_i \tag{4.5.7}$$

If λ_2 is almost the same as λ_1 in modulus, the reason for the slow convergence is clearly that their ratio has to be raised to a very large power before it becomes small. There is, however, a more direct way of eliminating this term if three successive values of the ratio are known. When (6) is broken off after the second term so that it becomes a geometrical progression the unknown K can be eliminated so that

$$\lambda_2/\lambda_1 = (r_{m+2} - r_{m+1})/(r_{m+1} - r_m) \tag{4.5.8}$$

and

$$\begin{aligned} \lambda_1 &= (r_{m+2}r_m - r_{m+1}^2)/(r_{m+2} - 2r_{m+1} + r_m) \\ &= \begin{vmatrix} r_{m+2} & r_{m+1} \\ r_{m+1} & r_m \end{vmatrix} \div \Delta^2 r_m \\ &= r_m - (\Delta r_m)^2/\Delta^2 r_m \end{aligned} \tag{4.5.9}$$

where the three forms are equivalent. This extrapolation process gives not only an accurate estimate of λ_1 but also an estimate of λ_2, though this is usually not very accurate. The eigenvector, also, can be estimated more accurately by a similar extrapolation and, if y_m is a component of the renormalized $\boldsymbol{v}_m$, other than the one which is always made unity, the extrapolation formula is

$$y_m - (\Delta y_m)^2/\Delta^2 y_m \tag{4.5.10}$$

In Table 4.1 the extrapolation process (10) is applied to the vectors at the stage marked by double rules. The improvement in accuracy is shown by the agreement of the normalized vectors. The estimates of λ_2 agree that it is negative, and the oscillation of the components confirms this, but the accuracy is very poor.

Despite its concern with the dominant eigenvalue, the power method can be adapted to find any eigenvalue. This is done by using, instead of the original matrix, some function of it such that the eigenvalue of interest becomes the dominant one. The simplest example is the use of

$$\boldsymbol{B} = \boldsymbol{A} + k\boldsymbol{I} \tag{4.5.11}$$

where, by choice of k, either the largest or the smallest eigenvalue of $\boldsymbol{A}$ becomes the one of largest modulus in $\boldsymbol{B}$. The eigenvectors are the same for both $\boldsymbol{A}$ and $\boldsymbol{B}$ and the eigenvalues differ only by the constant k. For the internal eigenvalues the function

$$(\boldsymbol{A} - k\boldsymbol{I})^{-1} \tag{4.5.12}$$

makes the eigenvalue nearest to k the largest. The calculation then proceeds by solving the equations

$$(\boldsymbol{A} - k\boldsymbol{I})\boldsymbol{v}_{m+1} = \boldsymbol{v}_m \tag{4.5.13}$$

If k is equal to an eigenvalue these equations are singular and cannot be solved. Consequently, the equations become ill-conditioned when k is close to an eigenvalue and it may be necessary to solve the equations to higher accuracy.

4.6 Properties of Eigenvalues

There are a number of properties of the eigenvalues and eigenvectors which are useful in extending and improving approximate methods. They also provide means whereby the distribution of eigenvalues can be estimated rapidly.

The trace rule (c.f. section 4.3) can be applied in various ways. The trace of the matrix itself determines the mean of the eigenvalues. The trace of the square of the matrix determines their variance. Higher moments of the distribution of eigenvalues could also be found but the labour involved increases and is not usually worthwhile. The same pair of traces can also be used to deduce the last two eigenvalues when all the others are known.

There is another theorem which can be used to locate the eigenvalues approximately but rapidly. It states that the eigenvalues of the matrix a_{ik} lie inside the set of circles (in the complex plane)

$$|z - a_{ii}| \leqslant \sum_{k \neq i} |a_{ik}| \tag{4.6.1}$$

For, if λ is an eigenvalue and $\boldsymbol{x}$ a corresponding eigenvector with x_l its dominant component, then the lth of the eigenvector equations is

$$\sum_{k \neq l} a_{lk} x_k = (\lambda - a_{ll}) x_l \tag{4.6.2}$$

so that

$$\sum_{k \neq l} |a_{lk}| |x_k| \geqslant |\lambda - a_{ll}| |x_l| \tag{4.6.3}$$

and, since $|x_l|$ is dominant, the result follows.

A number of powerful theorems apply only to Hermitian matrices.

Chief among these is Rayleigh's principle which states that, for varying $\boldsymbol{v}$, the ratio

$$e = \boldsymbol{v}^{\dagger}\boldsymbol{A}\boldsymbol{v}/\boldsymbol{v}^{\dagger}\boldsymbol{v} \tag{4.6.4}$$

is stationary when $\boldsymbol{v}$ is an eigenvector and e, then, is the eigenvalue. In particular, its maximum is the largest eigenvalue $\lambda_{\max}$ and its minimum the smallest $\lambda_{\min}$ and hence, for any $\boldsymbol{v}$,

$$\lambda_{\min} \leqslant \boldsymbol{v}^{\dagger}\boldsymbol{A}\boldsymbol{v}/\boldsymbol{v}^{\dagger}\boldsymbol{v} \leqslant \lambda_{\max} \tag{4.6.5}$$

The proof of this considers the continuous variation of $\boldsymbol{v}$ with some parameter α and then

$$\begin{aligned} \boldsymbol{v}^{\dagger}\boldsymbol{v}\frac{\partial e}{\partial \alpha} &= \left(\frac{\partial \boldsymbol{v}}{\partial \alpha}\right)^{\dagger}(\boldsymbol{A}\boldsymbol{v} - e\boldsymbol{v}) + (\boldsymbol{v}^{\dagger}\boldsymbol{A} - e\boldsymbol{v}^{\dagger})\frac{\partial \boldsymbol{v}}{\partial \alpha} \\ &= 2\,\mathrm{Re}\left(\frac{\partial \boldsymbol{v}}{\partial \alpha}\right)^{\dagger}(\boldsymbol{A}\boldsymbol{v} - e\boldsymbol{v}) \end{aligned} \tag{4.6.6}$$

so that the necessary and sufficient condition that e should be stationary for *any* such parameter is that

$$\boldsymbol{A}\boldsymbol{v} = e\boldsymbol{v} \tag{4.6.7}$$

This result can be used in several ways. By choosing some simple $\boldsymbol{v}$, for example, it is possible to estimate $\lambda_{\min}$ and $\lambda_{\max}$. A more accurate estimate can be found by using a $\boldsymbol{v}$ which contains a number of parameters and finding the maximum and minimum value of e attainable using these parameters. Another way of using this result is in estimating eigenvalues from approximate eigenvectors. Thus, when $\boldsymbol{v}$ is close to an eigenvector, the stationary property means that the error in $\boldsymbol{v}$ affects e only in the second order. When the power method is used for a Hermitian matrix, for example, the eigenvalue can be estimated much more accurately by using the value of e than by taking the ratio of one pair of components.

Some of these results can be extended to more general matrices, but only if two vectors $\boldsymbol{u}$ and $\boldsymbol{v}$ are used and the ratio is amended to

$$e = \tilde{\boldsymbol{u}}\boldsymbol{A}\boldsymbol{v}/\tilde{\boldsymbol{u}}\boldsymbol{v} \tag{4.6.8}$$

Now, if $\boldsymbol{v}$ is an approximation to the eigencolumn $\boldsymbol{x}_1$, whose eigenvalue is λ_1, so that

$$\boldsymbol{v} = \boldsymbol{x}_1 + \epsilon\boldsymbol{x} \tag{4.6.9}$$

and $\tilde{\boldsymbol{u}}$ is an approximation to the eigenrow $\tilde{\boldsymbol{y}}_1$ for the same eigenvalue so that

$$\boldsymbol{u} = \boldsymbol{y}_1 + \epsilon\boldsymbol{y} \tag{4.6.10}$$

then, because of the orthogonality relations, there is no loss of generality in taking

$$\tilde{\boldsymbol{y}}_1\boldsymbol{x} = \tilde{\boldsymbol{y}}\boldsymbol{x}_1 = 0 \tag{4.6.11}$$

Equations (9) (10) (11) substituted into (8) produce

$$e = \lambda_1 + \epsilon^2 \tilde{\boldsymbol{y}}(\boldsymbol{A} - \lambda_1 \boldsymbol{I})\boldsymbol{x}/(\tilde{\boldsymbol{y}}_1 \boldsymbol{x}_1 + \epsilon^2 \tilde{\boldsymbol{y}}\boldsymbol{x}) \tag{4.6.12}$$

so that the error in e is again of second order. Thus, in the power method, in addition to the vectors

$$\boldsymbol{v}_m = \boldsymbol{A}^m \boldsymbol{v}_0 \tag{4.6.13}$$

a second series

$$\boldsymbol{u}_m = (\tilde{\boldsymbol{A}})^m \boldsymbol{u}_0 \tag{4.6.14}$$

is needed and the estimate

$$e = \tilde{\boldsymbol{u}}_m \boldsymbol{v}_{m+1}/\tilde{\boldsymbol{u}}_m \boldsymbol{v}_m \tag{4.6.15}$$

has an error of the form

$$(\lambda_2/\lambda_1)^{2m} K \tag{4.6.16}$$

which is more rapidly convergent than (4.5.6).

4.7 Separation Theorem

Another general theorem which has many useful applications is the separation theorem. In its simplest form this theorem relates the eigenvalues of a matrix to the eigenvalues of another matrix formed by bordering it. If the first matrix is $\boldsymbol{B}$ then the second is

$$\boldsymbol{A} = \begin{pmatrix} a & \tilde{\boldsymbol{u}} \\ \boldsymbol{v} & \boldsymbol{B} \end{pmatrix} \tag{4.7.1}$$

and it is convenient to assume $\boldsymbol{B}$ to be diagonalized. The eigenvalue equation has the form

$$\begin{vmatrix} a - \lambda & u_1 & u_2 \\ v_1 & b_1 - \lambda & 0 \\ v_2 & 0 & b_2 - \lambda \\ \cdots & \cdots & \cdots \end{vmatrix} = 0 \tag{4.7.2}$$

and can be expanded as

$$a - \lambda = u_1 v_1 (b_1 - \lambda)^{-1} + u_2 v_2 (b_2 - \lambda)^{-1} + \ldots \tag{4.7.3}$$

This formula is valuable both in numerical calculation and in general argument. It becomes even simpler for a Hermitian matrix since all the b_i and all the λ are real and

$$\boldsymbol{u} = \boldsymbol{v}^* \tag{4.7.4}$$

so that the coefficients on the right of (3) are always positive. The general result follows that, for a Hermitian matrix, the effect of bordering is to push upwards the eigenvalues which are larger than a, to push down those lower than a and to produce an additional eigenvalue in the neighbourhood of a. This result is illustrated in Fig. 4.1 which is

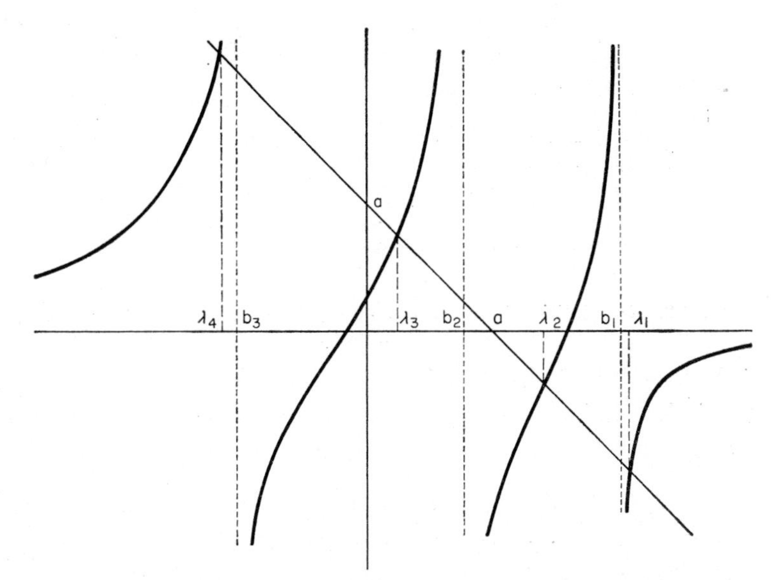

FIG. 4.1. Eigenvalues b_r of the submatrix separating the matrix eigenvalues λ_r.

typical of any Hermitian matrix. The functions plotted are the two sides of (3) and their intersections determine λ.

This theorem is often useful in locating the eigenvalues of a Hermitian matrix. If one row and the corresponding column is struck from the matrix the minor which remains has eigenvalues which lie between, or separate, those of the original matrix. The argument can be repeated with this minor and the minor which has two rows and columns removed. Eventually only a single diagonal element remains and the result of all the inequalities is that the diagonal elements of a matrix must all lie between the largest and smallest of the eigenvalues. The eigenvalues of the 2×2 minors whose leading diagonal elements are selected from the leading diagonal of the original matrix are also easy to calculate. The larger of these eigenvalues must lie between the largest and the second smallest of the eigenvalues of the original matrix and the smaller between its smallest and its second largest. By suitable choice of minors estimates of these four extreme eigenvalues can be obtained. The inequalities can be visualized from Fig. 4.2. A second way of applying these considerations is to use trial vectors rather than minors to estimate the eigenvalues. Thus for any vector $\boldsymbol{v}$, which is normalized

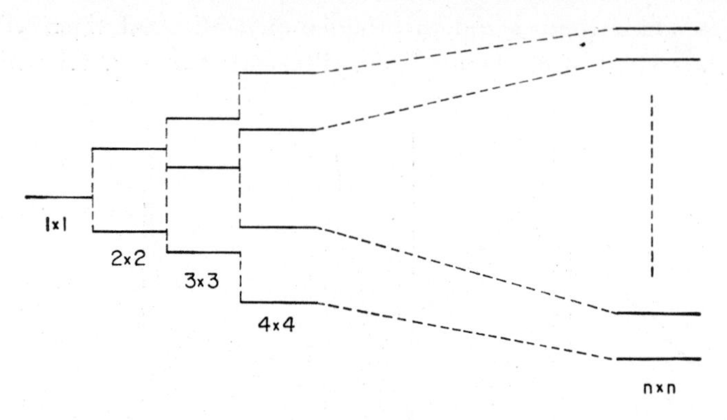

FIG. 4.2. Inequalities between the eigenvalues of a matrix and its leading minors.

to unity, the value of $\boldsymbol{v}^\dagger \boldsymbol{A} \boldsymbol{v}$ lies between the largest and smallest eigenvalues of $\boldsymbol{A}$. Similarly, two orthonormal vectors $\boldsymbol{u}$ and $\boldsymbol{v}$ define a 2×2 matrix

$$\begin{pmatrix} \boldsymbol{u}^\dagger \boldsymbol{A} \boldsymbol{u} & \boldsymbol{u}^\dagger \boldsymbol{A} \boldsymbol{v} \\ \boldsymbol{v}^\dagger \boldsymbol{A} \boldsymbol{u} & \boldsymbol{v}^\dagger \boldsymbol{A} \boldsymbol{v} \end{pmatrix} \tag{4.7.5}$$

whose eigenvalues satisfy the same inequalities as the minors above.

These uses of the separation theorem can be illustrated using the matrix

$$\boldsymbol{A} = \begin{pmatrix} 4 & 1 & 2 & 1 \\ 1 & 2 & 0 & 2 \\ 2 & 0 & 0 & 1 \\ 1 & 2 & 1 & 1 \end{pmatrix} \tag{4.7.6}$$

Inspection of the diagonal elements shows that one eigenvalue is greater than 4 and one is negative. The minor matrix

$$\begin{pmatrix} 4 & 1 \\ 1 & 2 \end{pmatrix} \tag{4.7.7}$$

shows that

$$\lambda_1 \geqslant 4.414 \geqslant \lambda_3 \, ; \qquad \lambda_2 \geqslant 1.586 \geqslant \lambda_4 \tag{4.7.8}$$

while the minor

$$\begin{pmatrix} 4 & 2 \\ 2 & 0 \end{pmatrix} \tag{4.7.9}$$

gives

$$\lambda_1 \geqslant 4.828 \geqslant \lambda_3 \, ; \qquad \lambda_2 \geqslant -0.828 \geqslant \lambda_4 \tag{4.7.10}$$

and

$$\begin{pmatrix} 0 & 1 \\ 1 & 1 \end{pmatrix} \tag{4.7.11}$$

gives

$$\lambda_1 \geqslant 1.618 \geqslant \lambda_3 \, ; \qquad \lambda_2 \geqslant -0.618 \geqslant \lambda_4 \tag{4.7.12}$$

so that, in addition to the inequalities implied by numbering,

$$\lambda_1 \geqslant 4.828\ ; \qquad \lambda_2 \geqslant 1.586\ ; \qquad \lambda_3 \leqslant 1.618\ ; \qquad \lambda_4 \leqslant -0.828 \qquad (4.7.13)$$

More accurate estimates are possible using trial vectors. The vector

$$\tilde{\boldsymbol{v}} = \sqrt{\tfrac{1}{7}}(2, 1, 1, 1) \qquad (4.7.14)$$

gives the result

$$\lambda_1 \geqslant 5\tfrac{6}{7} \qquad (4.7.15)$$

and with the vector

$$\tilde{\boldsymbol{u}} = \sqrt{\tfrac{1}{7}}(-1, 2, -1, 1) \qquad (4.7.16)$$

gives the 2×2 matrix

$$\tfrac{1}{7}\begin{pmatrix} 41 & 1 \\ 1 & 17 \end{pmatrix} \qquad (4.7.17)$$

which yields the inequalities

$$\lambda_1 \geqslant 5.863\ ; \qquad \lambda_2 \geqslant 2.423 \qquad (4.7.18)$$

The vector

$$\tilde{\ } = \sqrt{\tfrac{1}{7}}(-1, 1, 2, -1) \qquad (4.7.19)$$

similarly gives

$$\lambda_4 \leqslant -1\tfrac{2}{7} \qquad (4.7.20)$$

Thus, with comparatively little effort, reasonable estimates of the eigenvalues are obtained. The accurate values are

$$\lambda_1 = 5{\cdot}876 \quad \lambda_2 = 2{\cdot}558 \quad \lambda_3 = -0{\cdot}048 \quad \lambda_4 = -1{\cdot}386 \qquad (4.7.21)$$

4.8 Accuracy of Approximate Eigenvalues

Most methods of calculating eigenvalues produce sequences of approximate eigenvalues which converge to the true eigenvalue from one side only. This makes it difficult to judge, during the calculation, the accuracy being attained. The information required can be obtained, however, with very little extra computation.

The vector

$$\boldsymbol{Av} - \lambda\boldsymbol{v} \qquad (4.8.1)$$

vanishes, according to the definitions, only when $\boldsymbol{v}$ is an eigencolumn and λ its eigenvalue. The accuracy of an approximate $\boldsymbol{v}$ and λ can then be measured by the length of this vector in relation to the length of $\boldsymbol{v}$. This is written as

$$\sigma^2 = |\boldsymbol{Av} - \lambda\boldsymbol{v}|^2/|\boldsymbol{v}|^2 = (\boldsymbol{Av} - \lambda\boldsymbol{v})^\dagger(\boldsymbol{Av} - \lambda\boldsymbol{v})/\boldsymbol{v}^\dagger\boldsymbol{v} \qquad (4.8.2)$$

and so is also the mean square of the residuals of the eigenvector equations. Not only does σ^2 give a measure of the accuracy of the approximation, it also gives a method of improving the accuracy of $\boldsymbol{v}$ or λ by minimization. The practical advantages of minimizing σ^2 instead of using the Rayleigh ratio are that it applies equally well for any eigenvector and does not favour the largest or smallest and that its minimum value, zero, is known in advance. For a fixed $\boldsymbol{v}$, the value of λ which minimizes σ^2 can easily be shown to be

$$\lambda = \boldsymbol{v}^\dagger \boldsymbol{A}\boldsymbol{v}/\boldsymbol{v}^\dagger\boldsymbol{v} \tag{4.8.3}$$

and so the Rayleigh ratio has the property of minimizing σ^2 even for non-Hermitian matrices or intermediate eigenvalues where its more familiar properties are lost. When λ satisfies (3), the value of σ^2 can be written as

$$\begin{aligned}\sigma^2 &= \boldsymbol{v}^\dagger\boldsymbol{A}^\dagger\boldsymbol{A}\boldsymbol{v}/\boldsymbol{v}^\dagger\boldsymbol{v} - \lambda^*\lambda \\ &= |\boldsymbol{A}\boldsymbol{v}|^2/|\boldsymbol{v}|^2 - |\lambda|^2\end{aligned} \tag{4.8.4}$$

For a Hermitian matrix, the significance of σ^2 as a measure of accuracy can be put into a more precise form. If the vector $\boldsymbol{v}$ is expanded in terms of the eigenvectors of $\boldsymbol{A}$ as

$$\boldsymbol{v} = \sum_i v_i \boldsymbol{x}_i \tag{4.8.5}$$

then

$$\boldsymbol{A}\boldsymbol{v} - \lambda\boldsymbol{v} = \sum_i (\lambda_i - \lambda) v_i \boldsymbol{x}_i \tag{4.8.6}$$

where λ_i are the eigenvalues of $\boldsymbol{A}$. It follows that

$$\begin{aligned}|\boldsymbol{A}\boldsymbol{v} - \lambda\boldsymbol{v}|^2 = \sum_i |\lambda_i - \lambda|^2|v_i|^2 = |\lambda_r - \lambda|^2 \sum_i |v_i|^2 + \\ + \sum_i \{|\lambda_i - \lambda|^2 - |\lambda_r - \lambda|^2\}|v_i|^2\end{aligned} \tag{4.8.7}$$

where λ_r is the eigenvalue nearest to λ, the one for which $|\lambda_i - \lambda|$ is smallest. Since the term in braces in (7) is always positive it is always true that

$$|\boldsymbol{A}\boldsymbol{v} - \lambda\boldsymbol{v}|^2 \geqslant |\lambda_r - \lambda|^2|\boldsymbol{v}|^2 \tag{4.8.8}$$

and, hence, that

$$|\lambda_r - \lambda| \leqslant \sigma \tag{4.8.9}$$

Thus, for a Hermitian matrix, a true eigenvalue must lie within σ of the approximate one. This estimate of the accuracy of λ is useful only when λ becomes fairly accurate since σ is very sensitive to errors. It can become especially important in proving the distinctness of close eigenvalues.

4.9 The Jacobi Method

Two features common to most methods of calculating eigenvalues and eigenvectors are that they deal with the eigenvalues one at a time and that the basic method is modified from time to time, in accordance with the judgement of the computer, in order to improve convergence. The first feature means that the determination of all the eigenvalues may be slow, and, in some methods, subject to increasing rounding-off error. The second feature means that these methods are not readily programmed for electronic computers. The Jacobi, or rotation, method is in sharp contrast to this since, in it, all the eigenvalues and eigenvectors are calculated simultaneously by a simple uniform process which is easily programmed. On the other hand, for hand-computation, it is too laborious to be a good method, particularly if only a few eigenvalues and eigenvectors are required. It is most easily applied to a real symmetric matrix though it can be extended to some other types.

In the Jacobi method the eigenvector problem is regarded as one of diagonalizing a matrix. A real symmetric matrix $\boldsymbol{A}$ can be brought to diagonal form $\boldsymbol{D}$ by means of an orthogonal matrix $\boldsymbol{O}$ such that

$$\tilde{\boldsymbol{O}}\boldsymbol{A}\boldsymbol{O} = \boldsymbol{D} \tag{4.9.1}$$

(c.f. 4.3.10). The Jacobi method achieves this diagonalization by expressing $\boldsymbol{O}$ as a product of orthogonal matrices since the product of orthogonal matrices is an orthogonal matrix. Each of these matrices makes one element on each side of the diagonal zero though, of course, later matrices may make the element non-zero again. If the off-diagonal element is a_{ik} then the corresponding matrix is the improper rotation matrix

$$\boldsymbol{O}_{ik} = \begin{bmatrix} 1 & & & & & & & & \\ & \ddots & & & & & & & \\ & & 1 & & & & & & \\ & & & \cos\theta & \dots & \sin\theta & & & \\ & & & & 1 & & & & \\ & & & \vdots & \ddots & \vdots & & & \\ & & & & 1 & & & & \\ & & & \sin\theta & \dots & -\cos\theta & & & \\ & & & & & & 1 & & \\ & & & & & & & \ddots & \\ & & & & & & & & 1 \end{bmatrix} \tag{4.9.2}$$

where

$$\tan 2\theta = 2a_{ik}/(a_{ii} - a_{kk}) \tag{4.9.3}$$

i.e. all the off-diagonal elements vanish except the (ik)th and the (ki)th and the diagonal elements are unity except the ith and the kth. The resulting product is now

$$\tilde{\boldsymbol{O}}_{ik}\boldsymbol{A}\boldsymbol{O}_{ik} = \begin{bmatrix} a_{11} & \ldots & b_{1i} & \ldots & b_{1k} & \ldots & a_{1n} \\ \vdots & & \vdots & & \vdots & & \vdots \\ b_{i1} & \ldots & b_{ii} & \ldots & 0 & \ldots & b_{in} \\ \vdots & & \vdots & & \vdots & & \vdots \\ b_{k1} & \ldots & 0 & \ldots & b_{kk} & \ldots & b_{kn} \\ \vdots & & \vdots & & \vdots & & \vdots \\ a_{n1} & \ldots & b_{ni} & \ldots & b_{nk} & \ldots & a_{nn} \end{bmatrix} \tag{4.9.4}$$

i.e. the elements of $\boldsymbol{A}$ are unchanged except in the ith and kth rows and columns which become, for $r \neq i, k$,

$$\begin{aligned} b_{ri} &= a_{ri}\cos\theta + a_{rk}\sin\theta \\ b_{rk} &= a_{ri}\sin\theta - a_{rk}\cos\theta \\ b_{ir} &= a_{ir}\cos\theta + a_{kr}\sin\theta \\ b_{kr} &= a_{ir}\sin\theta - a_{kr}\cos\theta \\ b_{ii} &= a_{ii}\cos^2\theta + a_{ik}\sin 2\theta + a_{kk}\sin^2\theta \\ b_{kk} &= a_{ii}\sin^2\theta - a_{ik}\sin 2\theta + a_{kk}\cos^2\theta \\ b_{ik} &= b_{ki} = 0 \end{aligned} \tag{4.9.5}$$

Now, since

$$\begin{aligned} b_{ri}^2 + b_{rk}^2 &= a_{ri}^2 + a_{rk}^2 \\ b_{ii}^2 + b_{kk}^2 &= a_{ii}^2 + a_{kk}^2 + 2a_{ik}^2 \end{aligned} \tag{4.9.6}$$

the sum of the squares of all the elements in the matrix is unchanged by the transformation (c.f. 4.3.23) but the sum of the squares of the diagonal elements alone has increased. Thus, after each transformation, the sum of the squares of the off-diagonal elements is smaller and, if the process is repeated, the sum must eventually become zero so that the matrix is diagonal. The orthogonal matrix is then the product

$$\boldsymbol{O} = \prod_{i<k} \boldsymbol{O}_{ik} \tag{4.9.7}$$

and the columns of this are the eigencolumns.

In practice, this is similar to an iteration method and the basic step of eliminating an element has to be repeated several times for all the off-diagonal elements before the result converges to a diagonal matrix. The most rapid convergence is obtained by eliminating the elements in order of their magnitude since this reduces the sum of squares of the off-diagonal elements to the greatest extent. This selection is possible in hand-calculation but is slow on a machine and it is more usual, therefore, to treat the elements in turn.

There is one instance where the Jacobi method is useful in hand calculation. This is in applying a preliminary transformation to a matrix to remove some large off-diagonal elements and so improve the convergence of the method used to complete the solution. The easiest example is when a_{ii} and a_{kk} are equal since $\theta = 45°$ and the new elements are

$$\begin{aligned} b_{ri} &= b_{ir} = \sqrt{\tfrac{1}{2}}(a_{ri} + a_{rk}) \\ b_{rk} &= b_{kr} = \sqrt{\tfrac{1}{2}}(a_{ri} - a_{rk}) \\ b_{ii} &= a_{ii} + a_{ik} \\ b_{kk} &= a_{ii} - a_{ik} \end{aligned} \tag{4.9.8}$$

4.10 The Partition Method

The partition method is a method of finding eigenvalues and eigenvectors one by one, which is suitable both for machine and hand computation. It has the advantages over the power method that its convergence depends on the approximate eigenvalues, rather than the approximate eigenvectors, and so is usually more rapid, and that it does not need to be modified to yield the internal eigenvalues. It is simplest when applied to a real symmetric matrix, since all the numbers are then real, but it can be applied with slight modifications to any matrix.

The essential step in the method is the partitioning of the matrix into four parts so that the first part a is a single element

$$\boldsymbol{A} = \begin{pmatrix} a & \tilde{\boldsymbol{c}} \\ \boldsymbol{c} & \boldsymbol{B} \end{pmatrix} \tag{4.10.1}$$

The convergence will be more rapid if the matrix is rearranged so that a is close to the eigenvalue to be calculated but the process will converge without this rearrangement. It is even possible to find all the eigenvalues without adjusting the partitioning though it is more efficient to vary it. The eigenvector is partitioned in a way which conforms to this and is normalized so that the first component is unity, i.e.

$$\begin{pmatrix} 1 \\ \boldsymbol{u} \end{pmatrix} \tag{4.10.2}$$

The eigenvector equations are then

$$\begin{pmatrix} a & \tilde{\boldsymbol{c}} \\ \boldsymbol{c} & \boldsymbol{B} \end{pmatrix}\begin{pmatrix} 1 \\ \boldsymbol{u} \end{pmatrix} = e\begin{pmatrix} 1 \\ \boldsymbol{u} \end{pmatrix} \tag{4.10.3}$$

or, in separated form,

$$(\boldsymbol{B} - e\boldsymbol{I})\boldsymbol{u} = -\boldsymbol{c} \tag{4.10.4}$$

$$e = a + \tilde{\boldsymbol{c}}\boldsymbol{u} \tag{4.10.5}$$

In practice, the method begins with an estimate e_0 of the eigenvalue required, which need not be the dominant one, and then the inhomogeneous equations,

$$(\boldsymbol{B} - e_0\boldsymbol{I})\boldsymbol{u} = -\boldsymbol{c} \tag{4.10.6}$$

are solved for the corresponding approximation to $\boldsymbol{u}$. From this approximate eigenvector the new estimate of the eigenvalue is found using the Rayleigh ratio, since this minimizes σ^2,

$$e_1 = (a + \tilde{\boldsymbol{c}}\boldsymbol{u} + e_0\tilde{\boldsymbol{u}}\boldsymbol{u})/(1 + \tilde{\boldsymbol{u}}\boldsymbol{u}) \tag{4.10.7}$$

and the corresponding variance is

$$\sigma^2 = \tilde{\boldsymbol{u}}\boldsymbol{u}(a + \boldsymbol{c}\boldsymbol{u} - e_0)^2/(1 + \tilde{\boldsymbol{u}}\boldsymbol{u})^2 \tag{4.10.8}$$

The rapid convergence of this method is due primarily to the fact that e_1 is a much better approximation to the eigenvalue than (5). In order that (6) should be soluble by the simple methods it is necessary that e_0 should not be an eigenvalue of $\boldsymbol{B}$ and the convergence improves as e_0 becomes further from these eigenvalues since the equations are less ill-conditioned and $\boldsymbol{u}$ is smaller. The condition that, in the partitioning, a should be close to e_0 helps to meet this requirement. The convergence can be studied further using the separation theorem.

The calculation proceeds iteratively. The new estimate e_1 leads to a better estimate of $\boldsymbol{u}$ and, hence, to a better eigenvalue. This is repeated until the accuracy, judged from σ^2, is sufficient. If the changes in e_0 are small and the equations (6) not ill-conditioned it is sufficient to treat the change in e_0 as giving rise to a residual (c.f. 3.4.7) and solve for the change in $\boldsymbol{u}$.

To illustrate the practical form of the method, two eigenvalues of the matrix

$$\boldsymbol{A} = \left(\begin{array}{c|ccc} 4 & 1 & 0 & 0 \\ \hline 1 & 2 & 0 & 1 \\ 0 & 0 & 1 & 1 \\ 0 & 1 & 1 & 0 \end{array}\right) \tag{4.10.9}$$

will be calculated. The largest eigenvalue is estimated from the leading 2×2 minor to be larger than 4·4. This suggests trying $e_0 = 4{\cdot}4$ and the rest of the calculation is shown in Table 4.2. The next largest

TABLE 4.2

The partition method for the largest eigenvalue

$B-e_0I,\ -c$	$-2{\cdot}4$	0	1	-1	$-2{\cdot}4$
	0	$-3{\cdot}4$	1	0	$-2{\cdot}4$
	1	1	$-4{\cdot}4$	0	$-2{\cdot}4$
	$-2{\cdot}4$	0	1	-1	$-2{\cdot}4$
	0	$-3{\cdot}4$	1	0	$-2{\cdot}4$
	$-0{\cdot}4167$	$-0{\cdot}2941$	$-3{\cdot}6892$	$-0{\cdot}4167$	$-4{\cdot}1059$

$\tilde{u} = (0{\cdot}4637,\ 0{\cdot}0332,\ 0{\cdot}1129)$
$e_0 = 4{\cdot}4$
$a = 4$
$\tilde{c}u = 0{\cdot}4637$
$\tilde{u}u = 0{\cdot}2289$
$|\tilde{u}| = 0{\cdot}4784$
$e_1 = 4{\cdot}4518$
$\sigma = 0{\cdot}0248$

$B-e_0I,\ -c$	$-2{\cdot}45$	0	1	-1	$-2{\cdot}45$
	0	$-3{\cdot}45$	1	0	$-2{\cdot}45$
	1	1	$-4{\cdot}45$	0	$-2{\cdot}45$
	$-2{\cdot}45$	0	1	-1	$-2{\cdot}45$
	0	$-3{\cdot}45$	1	0	$-2{\cdot}45$
	$-0{\cdot}40816$	$-0{\cdot}28986$	$-3{\cdot}75198$	$-0{\cdot}40816$	$-4{\cdot}16014$

$\tilde{u} = (0{\cdot}45257,\ 0{\cdot}03153,\ 0{\cdot}10879)$
$e_0 = 4{\cdot}45$
$a = 4$
$\tilde{c}u = 0{\cdot}45231$
$\tilde{u}u = 0{\cdot}217649$
$|u| = 0{\cdot}46653$
$e_1 = 4{\cdot}451897$
$\sigma = 0{\cdot}000885$

eigenvalue is probably around 2 since this is the next largest diagonal element. With $a = 2$ the new partitioning is

$$\left(\begin{array}{c|ccc} 2 & 1 & 0 & 1 \\ \hline 1 & 4 & 0 & 0 \\ 0 & 0 & 1 & 1 \\ 1 & 0 & 1 & 0 \end{array}\right) \tag{4.10.10}$$

and the calculation starting with $e_0 = 2$ is shown in Table 4.3.

TABLE 4.3

The partition method for an inner eigenvalue

$\boldsymbol{B}-e_0\boldsymbol{I},\ -\boldsymbol{c}$	2	0	0	−1	1	1·85	0	0	−1	·85
	0	−1	1	0	0	0	−1·15	1	0	− ·15
	0	1	−2	−1	−2	0	1	−2·15	−1	−2·15
	2	0	0	−1	1	1·85	0	0	−1	·85
	0	−1	1	0	0	0	−1·15	1	0	− ·15
	0	−1	−1	−1	−2	0	−0·8696	−1·2804	−1	−2·2804

$\tilde{\boldsymbol{u}} =$	$(-\frac{1}{2}\quad 1\quad 1)$	$\tilde{\boldsymbol{u}} =$	$(-0{\cdot}5405,\ 0{\cdot}6791,\ 0{\cdot}7810)$
$e_0 =$	2	$e_0 =$	2·15
$a =$	2	$a =$	2
$\tilde{\boldsymbol{c}}\boldsymbol{u} =$	0·5	$\tilde{\boldsymbol{c}}\boldsymbol{u} =$	0·2405
$\tilde{\boldsymbol{u}}\boldsymbol{u} =$	2·25	$\tilde{\boldsymbol{u}}\boldsymbol{u} =$	1·3633
$\lvert\boldsymbol{u}\rvert =$	1·5	$\lvert\boldsymbol{u}\rvert =$	1·1676
$e_1 =$	2·1539	$e_1 =$	2·1883
$\sigma =$	0·2308	$\sigma =$	0·0447

If the convergence to the eigenvalue should be slow it can be improved by an extrapolation process. The extrapolated value can be shown to be

$$e = e_1 - \tfrac{1}{2} + \tfrac{1}{2}\{1 + 4(e_2 - e_1)\}^{\frac{1}{2}} \tag{4.10.11}$$

where e_1 and e_2 are consecutive values of the Rayleigh ratio.

In hand computation and for the extreme eigenvalues there is a modification of the method which is sometimes useful. It has the advantage of improving the approximate eigenvalue but, unfortunately, the eigenvector is less accurate and σ^2 is larger. The method above is interrupted after $\boldsymbol{u}$ has been calculated and a trial vector of the form

$$\boldsymbol{r} = x\begin{pmatrix}1\\0\end{pmatrix} + y\begin{pmatrix}0\\\boldsymbol{u}\end{pmatrix} \tag{4.10.12}$$

is considered. The stationary values of the Rayleigh ratio, as x and y vary, are given by

$$\begin{vmatrix} a - e & \tilde{\boldsymbol{c}}\boldsymbol{u} \\ \tilde{\boldsymbol{c}}\boldsymbol{u} & \tilde{\boldsymbol{u}}\boldsymbol{u}(e_0 - e) - \tilde{\boldsymbol{c}}\boldsymbol{u} \end{vmatrix} = 0 \tag{4.10.13}$$

All the terms in this quadratic are already known and the two values of e are easily calculated. Since the trial eigenvector has an additional degree of freedom over that used in the standard method the estimate of an extreme eigenvalue must be improved (c.f. 4.7.5) but an internal eigenvalue may behave quite differently. The second solution obtained from the quadratic may be used, in accordance with the separation theorem, as a limit to the next nearest eigenvalue.

4.11 The Convergence of Matrix Series

In section 4.3 a function of a matrix was defined generally as

$$f(\boldsymbol{A}) = \sum_r f(\lambda_r)\boldsymbol{P}_r \tag{4.11.1}$$

where $\boldsymbol{P}_r$ is the projection operator associated with λ_r. This definition simplifies considerably the discussion of the convergence of matrix series and enables more precise tests to be given.

From (1) it follows that $f(\boldsymbol{A})$ is defined if and only if $f(\lambda_r)$ exists for all the eigenvalues. For a function defined as a series this implies that all the λ_r must lie inside the circle of convergence of the series. Thus, for a binomial series such as

$$(1 + x)^{\frac{1}{2}} = 1 + \tfrac{1}{2}x - \tfrac{1}{8}x^2 + \tfrac{1}{16}x^3 - \dots \tag{4.11.2}$$

the circle of convergence is

$$|x| < 1 \tag{4.11.3}$$

and consequently the matrix series

$$(\boldsymbol{I} + \boldsymbol{A})^{\frac{1}{2}} = \boldsymbol{I} + \tfrac{1}{2}\boldsymbol{A} - \tfrac{1}{8}\boldsymbol{A}^2 + \tfrac{1}{16}\boldsymbol{A}^3 - \dots \tag{4.11.4}$$

will converge if all the eigenvalues satisfy

$$|\lambda_r| < 1 \tag{4.11.5}$$

If this series is used to find $\boldsymbol{B}^{\frac{1}{2}}$ by writing

$$\boldsymbol{B} = \boldsymbol{I} + \boldsymbol{A} \tag{4.11.6}$$

then the eigenvalues μ_r of $\boldsymbol{B}$ will have to satisfy

$$|\mu_r - 1| < 1 \tag{4.11.7}$$

for (4) to converge. A better procedure is to write

$$k\boldsymbol{B} = \boldsymbol{I} + \boldsymbol{A} \tag{4.11.8}$$

so that the condition becomes

$$|k\mu_r - 1| < 1 \tag{4.11.9}$$

and now, if k has the same sign as $\mu_{\max}$ and

$$|k| \leqslant |\mu_{\max}^{-1}| \tag{4.11.10}$$

where $\mu_{\max}$ is the eigenvalue whose modulus is largest, this condition is satisfied for the largest eigenvalues. The condition is violated, however, if one μ_r vanishes or if one is of the opposite sign to $\mu_{\max}$, i.e. $\boldsymbol{B}$ must be positive definite or negative definite. Even a rough estimate of $\mu_{\max}$ is sufficient to give an acceptable k and so the inequality (4.6.1), or the power method, can be used to give an estimated $\mu_{\max}$.

If x is real then the series (2) converges to the positive square root. Similarly the series (4) for a real symmetric matrix converges to the square root matrix all of whose eigenvalues are positive. If the whole family of square roots are needed it is simpler to use

$$\boldsymbol{B}^{\frac{1}{2}} = \sum_r \pm (\mu_r)^{\frac{1}{2}} \boldsymbol{P}_r \tag{4.11.11}$$

and since there is ambiguity of sign for each μ_r there are 2^n square root matrices. If there is degeneracy among the μ_r the number becomes infinite (see **13**, p. 85).

4.12 Commuting Matrices

When two matrices commute, relations are set up between their eigenvectors. A full analysis of these relations is most easily given using algebra theory but some of the results can be found by direct methods. These restricted results are discussed here and used to simplify numerical calculation.

If λ is a non-degenerate eigenvalue of $\boldsymbol{A}$, then the eigenvector equations,

$$\boldsymbol{A}\boldsymbol{x} = \lambda \boldsymbol{x} \tag{4.12.1}$$

have a solution $\boldsymbol{x}$ which is unique except for a normalizing factor. $\boldsymbol{C}$ is a matrix which commutes with $\boldsymbol{A}$, so that

$$\boldsymbol{C}\boldsymbol{A} = \boldsymbol{A}\boldsymbol{C} \tag{4.12.2}$$

and hence, using (1),

$$\boldsymbol{C}\boldsymbol{A}\boldsymbol{x} = \boldsymbol{A}(\boldsymbol{C}\boldsymbol{x}) = \lambda(\boldsymbol{C}\boldsymbol{x}) \tag{4.12.3}$$

Thus, if $\boldsymbol{C}\boldsymbol{x}$ does not vanish, it must be an eigenvector of $\boldsymbol{A}$ belonging to λ and so a multiple of $\boldsymbol{x}$ i.e.

$$\boldsymbol{C}\boldsymbol{x} = \mu \boldsymbol{x} \tag{4.12.4}$$

This means that $\boldsymbol{x}$ is a simultaneous eigenvector of $\boldsymbol{A}$ and $\boldsymbol{C}$. The eigenvalue μ may or may not be degenerate. The converse, that an eigenvector of $\boldsymbol{C}$ belonging to a non-degenerate eigenvalue is a simultaneous eigenvector, follows by interchanging $\boldsymbol{A}$ and $\boldsymbol{C}$. If λ is degenerate the situation becomes complicated but, if $\boldsymbol{A}$ is a normal matrix, it is possible to find eigenvectors which are simultaneous eigenvectors.

This theorem can be applied in calculating the eigenvectors of a matrix $\boldsymbol{A}$ if it is possible to find a matrix $\boldsymbol{C}$ which commutes with $\boldsymbol{A}$ (other than $\boldsymbol{C} = \boldsymbol{I}$) and is easier to diagonalize. The simplest example is when $\boldsymbol{C}$ is a permutation matrix. A matrix which is left invariant when two rows and the corresponding two columns are permuted commutes with the permutation matrix. Thus, for example,

$$\boldsymbol{A} = \begin{pmatrix} 6 & 1 & 3 & 2 \\ 1 & 5 & 1 & 4 \\ 3 & 1 & 6 & 2 \\ 2 & 4 & 2 & 0 \end{pmatrix} \tag{4.12.5}$$

commutes with

$$\boldsymbol{C} = \begin{pmatrix} 0 & 0 & 1 & 0 \\ 0 & 1 & 0 & 0 \\ 1 & 0 & 0 & 0 \\ 0 & 0 & 0 & 1 \end{pmatrix} \tag{4.12.6}$$

and $\boldsymbol{C}$ has a triply degenerate eigenvalue, 1, and a non-degenerate one, -1. The simultaneous eigenvector corresponds to the latter and is

$$\tilde{\boldsymbol{x}} = (1 \quad 0 \quad -1 \quad 0) \tag{4.12.7}$$

Another illustration of the theorem involves the projection operators of section 4.3. If $\tilde{\boldsymbol{y}}$ is the eigenrow of $\boldsymbol{A}$ belonging to λ then

$$\boldsymbol{P} = \boldsymbol{x}\tilde{\boldsymbol{y}} \tag{4.12.8}$$

and, using the eigenvalue equations,

$$\boldsymbol{AP} = \lambda\boldsymbol{x}\tilde{\boldsymbol{y}} = \boldsymbol{x}\tilde{\boldsymbol{y}}\boldsymbol{A} = \boldsymbol{PA} \tag{4.12.9}$$

Thus $\boldsymbol{P}$ commutes with $\boldsymbol{A}$ and, since its rank is one, its eigenvalues are all zero except one which is unity. The eigenvector corresponding to unity is therefore a simultaneous eigenvector.

4.13 Circulants and Pseudo-circulants

There is one type of matrix which occurs so frequently in the theory of hydrocarbons and also, in generalized form, in the theory of crystals that it deserves special mention. Very fortunately, it is possible to find all the eigenvectors and eigenvalues of these matrices easily. These are the matrices known as circulants and have the form

$$\boldsymbol{A} = \begin{pmatrix} a & b & c & \ldots & z \\ z & a & b & c & \ldots \\ & & \ldots & & \\ c & \ldots & & a & b \\ b & c & \ldots & z & a \end{pmatrix} \tag{4.13.1}$$

i.e. the elements are equal in lines parallel to the leading diagonal and circulate from the end back to the beginning. This circulation ensures that $\boldsymbol{A}$ commutes with the permutation matrix $\boldsymbol{C}$ which permutes the elements in cyclic order viz.

$$\boldsymbol{C} = \begin{pmatrix} 0 & 1 & 0 & \dots & 0 \\ 0 & 0 & 1 & \dots & 0 \\ & & \dots & & \\ 0 & 0 & & \dots & 1 \\ 1 & 0 & & \dots & 0 \end{pmatrix} \tag{4.13.2}$$

In fact the circulant can be expressed immediately as a polynomial in $\boldsymbol{C}$

$$\boldsymbol{A} = a\boldsymbol{I} + b\boldsymbol{C} + c\boldsymbol{C}^2 + \dots \tag{4.13.3}$$

The eigenvalue equation for $\boldsymbol{C}$ has the simple form

$$\mu^n = 1 \tag{4.13.4}$$

where n is the order of the matrix, and so its eigenvalues are the nth roots of unity, each non-degenerate. It is convenient to use

$$\mathrm{e}^{\mathrm{i}k} \tag{4.13.5}$$

as a typical eigenvalue of the typical matrix and eventually to put

$$k = \begin{cases} 0, \pm 2\pi/n, \pm 4\pi/n, \dots, \pi & \text{if } n \text{ even} \\ 0, \pm 2\pi/n, \pm 4\pi/n, \dots, \pm(n-1)\pi/n & \text{if } n \text{ odd} \end{cases} \tag{4.13.6}$$

The eigencolumn corresponding to this is

$$\tilde{\boldsymbol{v}}(k) = (1, \quad \mathrm{e}^{\mathrm{i}k}, \quad \mathrm{e}^{2\mathrm{i}k}, \dots) \tag{4.13.7}$$

and the eigenrow is

$$\tilde{\boldsymbol{u}}(k) = (1, \quad \mathrm{e}^{-\mathrm{i}k}, \quad \mathrm{e}^{-2\mathrm{i}k}, \dots) \tag{4.13.8}$$

Thus, the matrix $\boldsymbol{A}$ has the typical eigenvalue

$$\lambda(k) = a + b\,\mathrm{e}^{\mathrm{i}k} + c\,\mathrm{e}^{2\mathrm{i}k} + \dots \tag{4.13.9}$$

which is a Fourier series in exponential form. Often $\boldsymbol{A}$ is also real and symmetric so that

$$\boldsymbol{A} = a\boldsymbol{I} + b(\boldsymbol{C} + \boldsymbol{C}^{-1}) + c(\boldsymbol{C}^2 + \boldsymbol{C}^{-2}) + \dots \tag{4.13.10}$$

and its eigenvalue is

$$\lambda(k) = a + 2b\cos k + 2c\cos 2k + \dots \tag{4.13.11}$$

These eigenvalues are doubly degenerate, with eigencolumns $\boldsymbol{v}(k)$ and $\boldsymbol{v}(-k)$, except when $k = 0$ or π.

The definition of a circulant can be generalized to include matrices which can be partitioned so that the blocks form a circulant, e.g.

$$\boldsymbol{M} = \begin{pmatrix} \boldsymbol{A} & \boldsymbol{B} & \boldsymbol{C} \dots & \boldsymbol{Z} \\ \boldsymbol{Z} & \boldsymbol{A} & \boldsymbol{B} \dots & \\ & & \dots & \\ \boldsymbol{B} & \boldsymbol{C} & \dots & \boldsymbol{A} \end{pmatrix} \tag{4.13.12}$$

The typical eigencolumn is now written as

$$\boldsymbol{v}(k) = \begin{pmatrix} \boldsymbol{w} \\ \mathrm{e}^{\mathrm{i}k}\boldsymbol{w} \\ \mathrm{e}^{2\mathrm{i}k}\boldsymbol{w} \\ \vdots \end{pmatrix} \tag{4.13.13}$$

where $\boldsymbol{w}(k)$ is a subvector. The eigenvector equation reduces to

$$(\boldsymbol{A} + \boldsymbol{B}\,\mathrm{e}^{\mathrm{i}k} + \boldsymbol{C}\,\mathrm{e}^{2\mathrm{i}k} + \dots)\boldsymbol{w}(k) = \lambda(k)\boldsymbol{w}(k) \tag{4.13.14}$$

and this has to be solved by some appropriate method for the whole range of values of k.

The same basic ideas can be adapted to deal with pseudo-circulants. These are matrices, which occur for chain rather than cyclic molecules, and have the form

$$\boldsymbol{A} = \begin{pmatrix} a & b & 0 & \dots & & 0 \\ b & a & b & 0 & \dots & 0 \\ & & \dots & & & \\ 0 & & \dots & & b & a \end{pmatrix} \tag{4.13.15}$$

More general possibilities can be included by considering a polynomial in $\boldsymbol{A}$ but the elements are no longer equal in diagonal lines. Since this matrix $\boldsymbol{A}$ can be considered as a block partitioned out of a larger circulant it is not surprising that the eigenvalues have the same typical form

$$\lambda(k) = a + 2b \cos k \tag{4.13.16}$$

The eigenvectors are, however, somewhat changed. The first of the eigenvector equations is

$$(a - \lambda)v_1 + bv_2 = 0 \tag{4.13.17}$$

whereas, for the circulant, it would be

$$bv_0 + (a - \lambda)v_1 + bv_2 = 0 \tag{4.13.18}$$

and to make these conform v_0 has to be zero. Similarly the final equation conforms if v_{n+1} is also zero. Thus the pseudo-circulant eigenvector equations become circulant ones when these two conditions are satisfied. To satisfy the first condition the degeneracy between the

$\boldsymbol{v}(k)$ and $\boldsymbol{v}(-k)$ of the circulant is used and the appropriate combination is obviously

$$\boldsymbol{x}(k) = \begin{pmatrix} \sin k \\ \sin 2k \\ \sin 3k \\ \vdots \end{pmatrix} \tag{4.13.19}$$

The second condition will be satisfied if

$$\sin (n+1)k = 0 \tag{4.13.20}$$

so that k takes the values

$$k = \pi/(n+1),\ 2\pi/(n+1), \ldots ,\ 2n\pi/(n+1) \tag{4.13.21}$$

and the eigenvalues are $\lambda(s\pi/(n+1))$ and are non-degenerate.

EXERCISES

1. Show that the eigenvalues and eigenvectors of

$$\begin{pmatrix} 1 & 2 & 0 \\ 2 & 3 & 2 \\ 0 & 2 & 1 \end{pmatrix}$$

can be found using the direct methods of 4·4.

2. Show that the eigenvalues of an antihermitian matrix are pure imaginaries and those of a unitary matrix have unit modulus. How are their eigenrows and eigencolumns related?

3. Verify that the matrix $\begin{pmatrix} 1 & 0 \\ 1 & 1 \end{pmatrix}$ has a doubly degenerate eigenvalue but only one eigenvector.

4. Find four matrices whose squares are each $\begin{pmatrix} 5 & 4 \\ 4 & 5 \end{pmatrix}$.

5. Verify that $\lambda = 0$ is an eigenvalue of

$$A = \begin{pmatrix} 1 & 1 & -1 \\ 0 & 2 & 2 \\ -1 & 0 & 2 \end{pmatrix}$$

and use the traces of A and A^2 to find the remaining eigenvalues.

6. A real symmetric matrix A is defined as *positive definite* if $\tilde{\boldsymbol{x}}A\boldsymbol{x} > 0$ for any real $\boldsymbol{x}$. Show (i) that all its eigenvalues $\lambda_r > 0$ (ii) that if a matrix has all its eigenvalues $\lambda_r > 0$ it is positive definite.

7. Use the power method to find the largest eigenvalue and eigenvector of

$$\begin{pmatrix} 5 & 6 & 2 & 2 \\ 6 & 10 & 3 & 3 \\ 2 & 3 & 1 & 2 \\ 2 & 3 & 2 & 1 \end{pmatrix}; \qquad \begin{pmatrix} 63 & 16 & 23 & 7 \\ 16 & 38 & 12 & 4 \\ 23 & 12 & 49 & 7 \\ 7 & 4 & 7 & 33 \end{pmatrix}$$

8. Find the smallest eigenvalue of the matrix (4.7.6) using the power method.

9. Solve graphically, for a number of values of x in the range -1 to 3,

$$\begin{vmatrix} x-\lambda & 1 & 2 & 1 \\ 1 & 2-\lambda & 0 & 0 \\ 2 & 0 & 1-\lambda & 0 \\ 1 & 0 & 0 & -\lambda \end{vmatrix} = 0$$

10. Diagonalize, using the Jacobi method,

$$\begin{pmatrix} 2\sqrt{2} & \sqrt{2} & 1 \\ \sqrt{2} & 2\sqrt{2} & 1 \\ 1 & 1 & 3\sqrt{2} \end{pmatrix}$$

11. Find the second largest eigenvalue of the matrix (4.7.6) by the partition method.

12. Use (4.11.1) to prove that a normal matrix satisfies its own eigenvalue equation. (Cayley–Hamilton theorem.)

13. Show that the matrix $\begin{pmatrix} 1 & 0 \\ 0 & 1 \end{pmatrix}$ has the square roots $\pm\begin{pmatrix} 1 & 0 \\ 0 & 1 \end{pmatrix}$ and $\pm\begin{pmatrix} \cos\theta & \sin\theta \\ \sin\theta & -\cos\theta \end{pmatrix}$

14. Verify that $\boldsymbol{C}$ commutes with $\boldsymbol{A}$ and, hence, find all the eigenvalues of $\boldsymbol{A}$, where

$$\boldsymbol{C} = \begin{pmatrix} 0 & 1 & -1 \\ 1 & 0 & -1 \\ -1 & -1 & 0 \end{pmatrix}, \boldsymbol{A} = \begin{pmatrix} -2 & -1 & 6 \\ -1 & 1 & 9 \\ 6 & 9 & 6 \end{pmatrix}$$

15. By showing that it is a pseudo-circulant, find all the eigenvalues of

$$\begin{pmatrix} 3 & 3 & 1 & 0 & 0 \\ 3 & 4 & 3 & 1 & 0 \\ 1 & 3 & 4 & 3 & 1 \\ 0 & 1 & 3 & 4 & 3 \\ 0 & 0 & 1 & 3 & 3 \end{pmatrix}$$

16. Find the eigenvalues of the circulant

$$\begin{pmatrix} 0 & a & 0 & \dots & & b \\ a & 0 & b & 0 & \dots & 0 \\ 0 & b & 0 & a & 0 & \dots \\ & & \dots & & & \end{pmatrix}$$

and discuss the changes as b approaches a.

17. *Generalized eigenvalues* λ and eigenvectors $\boldsymbol{x}$ can be defined as solutions of

$$(\boldsymbol{A} - \lambda \boldsymbol{S})\boldsymbol{x} = \boldsymbol{0}$$

for given matrices $\boldsymbol{A}$ and $\boldsymbol{S}$. If both $\boldsymbol{A}$ and $\boldsymbol{S}$ are Hermitian, and orthogonality of $\boldsymbol{x}$ and $\boldsymbol{y}$ now means

$$\boldsymbol{x}^\dagger \boldsymbol{S}\boldsymbol{y} = 0$$

prove that Theorem B still applies.

18. A matrix has the partitioned form $\boldsymbol{A} = \begin{pmatrix} 0 & \boldsymbol{B} \\ \tilde{\boldsymbol{B}} & 0 \end{pmatrix}$, where $\boldsymbol{B}$ is a rectangular matrix with real elements. By considering $\boldsymbol{A}^2$, or otherwise, prove that
(i) The non-zero eigenvalues occur in pairs as $\pm\lambda$
(ii) λ^2 may be determined from either $\tilde{\boldsymbol{B}}\boldsymbol{B}$ or $\boldsymbol{B}\tilde{\boldsymbol{B}}$
(iii) the eigenvectors are determined by the eigenvectors of $\tilde{\boldsymbol{B}}\boldsymbol{B}$ or $\boldsymbol{B}\tilde{\boldsymbol{B}}$
(iv) eigenvectors which have $\lambda = 0$ have many vanishing components
(v) orthogonal matrices $\boldsymbol{O}$ and $\boldsymbol{P}$ can be found so that $\tilde{\boldsymbol{O}}\boldsymbol{B}\boldsymbol{P}$ is diagonal.

19. If matrices C and A satisfy $CA = -AC + kC$, for constant k, prove that
(i) the non-zero eigenvalues occur in pairs as $\frac{1}{2}k \pm \lambda$
(ii) C and A^2 have simultaneous eigenvectors
(iii) one example is $A = \begin{pmatrix} kI & B \\ B & kI \end{pmatrix}$; $C = \begin{pmatrix} I & 0 \\ 0 & -I \end{pmatrix}$.

20. A *principal vector* is defined as a vector v satisfying

$$(A - \lambda I)^r \, v = 0$$

for an eigenvalue λ and some integer r. Find all the principal columns and principal rows of

$$A = \begin{pmatrix} 2 & 0 & 0 \\ 1 & 2 & 0 \\ 0 & 1 & 2 \end{pmatrix}$$

21. A matrix is *nilpotent* if $A^r = 0$ for an integer r other than zero. Form the direct products of the principal columns and principal rows in 20 and show that some are nilpotent. Express A as a sum of these direct products.

22. A *stochastic* matrix p_{ij} has all its elements real and positive and

$$\sum_i p_{ij} = 1, \quad \text{all } j$$

Prove that
(i) it has 1 as an eigenvalue
(ii) all its eigenvalues π satisfy $0 \leqslant |\pi| \leqslant 1$
(iii) if $v_n = P^n v_0$ then v_n tends to a limit independent of v_0 in general but that, if $\pi = 1$ is degenerate, the limit depends on v_0 and, if another eigenvalue has $|\pi| = 1$, v_n may oscillate.

23. If a matrix has distinct eigenvalues, prove that the sum of its projection operators is the unit matrix and, hence, that an arbitrary column can be expanded as a linear combination of eigencolumns.

CHAPTER 5

TENSOR ALGEBRA

5.1 Introduction

Tensor algebra is needed in two different types of chemical problem. The first and most obvious illustration of its necessity is that many molecular properties are tensors. Thus, the dipole moment of a molecule behaves as a vector and is treated by familiar vector techniques, but its quadrupole and octupole moments, its polarizability and the nuclear quadrupole moments are tensors and need more elaborate techniques. The second point where tensor algebra is needed is in the theory of atomic and molecular wavefunctions since these are tensors. The problem of classifying wavefunctions requires group theory for a full discussion but a preliminary discussion can be given in terms of the transformation properties of tensors.

It is convenient, in this chapter, to return to the more general non-orthogonal bases of the first chapter. This means that contravariant and covariant components are distinct and are denoted by affices and suffices. The convenience, which compensates for this extra complication, is that the transformation properties of the components can all be summed up in the conventions governing the use of indices.

5.2 Tensors

Entities whose components have one or two indices have been used freely in earlier chapters and, in the first instance, tensors are the generalization of these to any number of indices. Thus a vector becomes a tensor of the first order and a matrix one of the second order. A third order tensor will have three indices and its components can be imagined as a three-dimensional array of numbers. Higher order tensors need more indices and more imagination but are not usually more difficult to manipulate since it is only certain cross-sections of the array which are needed at any one time. For completeness a scalar quantity is considered as a zero-order tensor.

Much more is included in the idea of a tensor than just the number of indices possessed by its components. In discussing vectors it was necessary to distinguish between several different entities which are all, at times, referred to as vectors. Thus the abstract vector x is distinguished from its components, whether written as a column $\boldsymbol{x}$, or individually as x_i. The first is, in geometrical terms, a line segment directed from the origin or, in physical terms, a displacement, a velocity, a force etc. whereas the second is a set of numbers relating it to some given basic set of vectors e_i. On the other hand, once the basic set is specified a knowledge of the components, x_i, is equivalent to a knowledge of x so that the components are legitimately called the vector. The other distinction drawn earlier was between the contravariant components x^i and the covariant components x_i of the same vector. Except when the basis vectors are orthonormal, these are different sets of numbers which relate the vector to the basis in different ways and transform according to different equations when the basis is transformed. Similar distinctions must now be made for tensors of any order.

The full definition of a tensor is most conveniently given in terms of its components and their transformation properties when the basis is transformed from the original e_k to the new $\bar{\mathsf{e}}_i$, where

$$\bar{\mathsf{e}}_i = t_i{}^k \mathsf{e}_k \tag{5.2.1}$$

An sth order tensor is defined to be an entity with n^s components which transform, when the basis is subject to the arbitrary (but non-singular) transformation t_i^k, as

$$\bar{x}^{ijk\ldots}_{abc\ldots} = T^i_l T^j_m T^k_n \ldots t^d_a t^e_b t^f_c \ldots x^{lmn\ldots}_{def\ldots} \tag{5.2.2}$$

with

$$T^i_j t^j_k = \delta^i_k \tag{5.2.3}$$

as in (1.10.13). If there are r affices and $(s - r)$ suffices these $x^{lmn\ldots}_{def\ldots}$ are the r fold contravariant components of the tensor. The arithmetical properties of tensors follow immediately from this definition. Thus, components of the same type (e.g. r fold contravariant and $(s - r)$ fold covariant) can be added, or subtracted, each to each to give the components of a new tensor of the same type. Similarly, multiplication of all the components of a tensor by the same scalar will not disrupt the transformation equations and so will produce a new tensor. In particular there is always a zero tensor of any order and all of its components are zero in every basis system. The final result is that, as far as addition and multiplication by a scalar are concerned, tensors of order s behave like vectors in a space of n^s dimensions.

A more elaborate operation is the product of two tensors, not necessarily of the same order. This product is formed by multiplying a component of one by a component of another in all possible pairs and is sometimes called the direct product, the Kronecker product or the tensor product. The product of x^a_{bc} and y^{fg}_h, for example, is

$$z^{afg}_{bch} = x^a_{bc} y^{fg}_h \tag{5.2.4}$$

It is easily shown, using the transformation equations, that the product transforms as a tensor whose order is the sum of the orders of the two original tensors.

The other operation needed in tensor algebra is contraction. It is described formally as the identification of two indices of opposite type but, because of the summation convention, this implies a sum over the corresponding components. Contraction produces a tensor whose order is reduced by two; for, if the tensor is $x^{lmn\ldots}_{def\ldots}$ with the transformation equation (2), its contraction satisfies

$$\begin{aligned} \bar{x}^{ijk\ldots}_{ibc\ldots} &= (T^i_l t^d_i) T^j_m T^k_n \ldots t^e_b t^f_c x^{lmn\ldots}_{def\ldots} \\ &= T^j_m T^k_n \ldots t^e_b t^f_c x^{lmn}_{lef} \end{aligned} \tag{5.2.5}$$

since

$$T^i_l t^d_i = \delta^d_l \tag{5.2.6}$$

Equation (5) is the transformation law for a tensor which is $(r-1)$ fold contravariant and $(s-r-1)$ fold covariant.

These two operations, of multiplication and contraction, include and generalize many of the operations used earlier. The direct product of two vectors, whose components are a_i and b^j, is $a_i b^j$ in agreement with (2.8.1) and the contraction of this second order tensor is the scalar product $a_i b^i$.

Similarly the matrix product $\boldsymbol{AB}$ is the contraction of the direct product

$$a_{ij} b^{jk} \tag{5.2.7}$$

while modifications such as $\tilde{\boldsymbol{A}}\boldsymbol{B}$ need no new symbols but become

$$a_{ji} b^{jk} \tag{5.2.8}$$

The operation of taking the trace of a matrix is also a contraction,

$$\mathrm{Tr}\,\boldsymbol{A} = a_i{}^i \tag{5.2.9}$$

and this enables a series of invariants, i.e. quantities independent of the basis, to be written down viz.

$$a^i_i\,; \quad a^j_i a^i_j\,; \quad a^j_i a^k_j a^i_k\,; \ldots \tag{5.2.10}$$

and these are the traces of powers of A already used in several connections. The fact that some of these relations involve one type of component and some a different type shows that the generalization from an orthonormal basis to a more general one will be easy only if one type of component can be deduced from another type of component of the same tensor.

5.3 Polyadics

Some insight into the nature of a tensor itself, as distinct from its components, can be gained by considering examples in which tensors are constructed from vectors. The relation between a vector and its components is

$$a = a^i \mathbf{e}_i \tag{5.3.1}$$

where $\mathbf{e}_i$ are the basis vectors. The direct product of two vectors is written

$$ab = (a^i \mathbf{e}_i)(b^j \mathbf{e}_j) = (a^i b^j)(\mathbf{e}_i \mathbf{e}_j) \tag{5.3.2}$$

so that the components of the second order tensor have the same relation to the products $\mathbf{e}_i\mathbf{e}_j$ as the components of a first order tensor have to $\mathbf{e}_i$. This product of two basis vectors is just their juxtaposition and is called a dyad. An expression for a general second order tensor in terms of these dyads,

$$A = a^{ij} \mathbf{e}_i \mathbf{e}_j \tag{5.3.3}$$

is called a dyadic. Since this involves the double contraction of the contravariant components into the two covariant basis vectors the result is invariant and A is the tensor in a form independent of the basis. The nature of the dyad is further illuminated by considering its scalar product into a vector. Since the scalar product means that

$$(\mathbf{e}_i \mathbf{e}_j) \cdot a = \mathbf{e}_i(\mathbf{e}_j \cdot a) = a_j \mathbf{e}_i \tag{5.3.4}$$

the dyad operates on the vector to produce another vector. The simplest dyads to interpret are the mixed dyads $\mathbf{e}^i\mathbf{e}_j$ since, for $i = j$, they are projection operators

$$(\mathbf{e}^i \mathbf{e}_i) \cdot (\mathbf{e}^i \mathbf{e}_i) = \mathbf{e}^i(\mathbf{e}_i \cdot \mathbf{e}^i)\mathbf{e}_i = \mathbf{e}^i \mathbf{e}_i \quad \text{(no summation)} \tag{5.3.5}$$

and, for $i \neq j$, nilpotents (c.f. p. 86)

$$(\mathbf{e}^i \mathbf{e}_j) \cdot (\mathbf{e}^i \mathbf{e}_j) = \mathbf{e}^i(\mathbf{e}_j \cdot \mathbf{e}^i)\mathbf{e}_j = 0 \tag{5.3.6}$$

Thus the second order tensor is an operator which acts on vectors to produce other vectors and does so in a linear way. Physically, such operators include rotations, reflections, projections and homogeneous strains. The second order tensor is distinguished by the fact that it can also have a scalar product with two vectors. This can be denoted either by placing the vectors on either side as

$$a \,.\, A \,.\, b \tag{5.3.7}$$

or on one side with a colon notation

$$A : (ba) \tag{5.3.8}$$

This notation makes the order of the vectors in a dyadic important since it determines which vectors appear in these scalar products. The convention above implies that

$$a \,.\, A \,.\, b = A : (ba) = (ba) : A \tag{5.3.9}$$

but that these differ from

$$b \,.\, A \,.\, a = A : (ab) = (ab) : A \tag{5.3.10}$$

It is also possible to take the double scalar product of two second order tensors

$$A : B \tag{5.3.11}$$

One use of this double scalar product is to relate the different types of component of a second order tensor. The components of a tensor are found by a double scalar product into the appropriate dyads just as the vector components can be found by a single scalar product. Thus, from (5) and the relation between the reciprocal vectors,

$$A : (e^r e^s) = a^{ij}(e_i e_j) : (e^r e^s) = a^{ij}(e_i \,.\, e^s)(e_j \,.\, e^r) = a^{sr} \tag{5.3.12}$$

similarly, by defining

$$\begin{aligned} a_s{}^r = A : (e^r e_s) &= a^{ij}(e_i e_j) : (e^r e_s) = a^{ij}(e_i \,.\, e_s)(e_j \,.\, e^r) \\ &= a^{ir} g_{is} \end{aligned} \tag{5.3.13}$$

the formula for lowering an index is deduced. This can be generalized to give

$$a_{sr} = a^{ij} g_{is} g_{jr} \tag{5.3.14}$$

In a parallel way the scalar products g^{ij} can be used to raise an index as in the equation

$$a_s{}^r = a_{si} g^{ir} \tag{5.3.15}$$

The particular second order tensor defined by the dyadic

$$I = e^i e_i \tag{5.3.16}$$

is known as the unit tensor because of its property of leaving a vector unchanged, since

$$I \cdot a = e^i(e_i \cdot a) = e^i a_i = a \tag{5.3.17}$$

The mixed components of I are δ^i_k, its covariant components g_{ik} and its contravariant components g^{ik}.

Most of these considerations are readily generalized to tensors of arbitrary order. The tensor X, whose components $x^{lmn\ldots}_{abc\ldots}$ are known, is defined by the polyadic†

$$X = x^{lmn\ldots}_{abc\ldots}\, e^a e^b e^c \ldots e_l e_m e_n \ldots \tag{5.3.18}$$

In a polyad the order of the vectors is significant only when the scalar products are considered and any of its basis vectors can be multiplied into another vector. A possible notation to overcome this difficulty is to write the vector below the appropriate part of the polyad with the scalar product dot between. Thus (12) becomes

$$\begin{array}{c} A \\ \cdot\cdot \\ e^s e^r \end{array} = a^{sr} \tag{5.3.19}$$

and the three possible products of a triad and a vector are

$$\begin{array}{c} e^r e^s e_t \\ \cdot \\ a \end{array} = a^r e^s e_t; \quad \begin{array}{c} e^r e^s e_t \\ \cdot \\ a \end{array} = a^s e^r e_t; \quad \begin{array}{c} e^r e^s e_t \\ \cdot \\ a \end{array} = a_t e^r e^s \tag{5.3.20}$$

By repeating the argument above, it can be shown that the indices of tensor components can always be lowered by contraction into g_{ik} and raised by contraction into g^{ik}. One function of these higher order tensors is, then, to operate on vectors to yield tensors. A third order tensor, as in (20), acts on a vector to produce a second order tensor and would be needed, for example, to calculate the change in a molecular quadrupole moment due to a small displacement of a nucleus. More generally, tensors operate on tensors to give tensors. The most general linear relation between two second order tensors, for example, is a fourth order tensor.

5.4 Symmetry Properties of Tensors

The components of a tensor are said to be symmetric with respect to a pair of indices of the same type if they are unchanged when the indices

† It is useful, in manuscript, to denote the vectors by one underline and the rth order tensor by r underlines. The number of underlines should then balance on both sides of an equation except when scalar products are involved.

are interchanged. The components a_{ijk} are symmetric with respect to the first pair of indices when

$$a_{ijk} = a_{jik} \tag{5.4.1}$$

It can easily be shown that when this relation holds in one basis system it will be preserved on transforming to any other basis system. In particular it will hold when the indices are raised or lowered simultaneously so that (1) implies

$$a^{ij}{}_k = a^{ji}{}_k \tag{5.4.2}$$

This means that symmetry is a property of the tensor itself.

In a similar way a tensor is defined to be skew-symmetric or skew if, when two indices of the same type are interchanged, its components are equal in magnitude but opposite in sign. Thus B is skew with respect to its first pair of indices when

$$b_{ijk} = -b_{jik} \tag{5.4.3}$$

This property is also preserved on transformation of basis.

These symmetry properties are particularly important for second order tensors since these have only one pair of indices. Any second order tensor can be expressed as the sum of a symmetric tensor and a skew tensor. This is proved by constructing the two tensors for, if A has components a_{ik}, its symmetric part is

$$b_{ik} = \tfrac{1}{2}(1 + P_{12})a_{ik} = \tfrac{1}{2}(a_{ik} + a_{ki}) \tag{5.4.4}$$

its skew part

$$c_{ik} = \tfrac{1}{2}(1 - P_{12})a_{ik} = \tfrac{1}{2}(a_{ik} - a_{ki}) \tag{5.4.5}$$

where P_{12} is the operation of permuting the indices, and clearly

$$a_{ik} = b_{ik} + c_{ik} \tag{5.4.6}$$

The operators $\frac{1}{2}(1 \pm P_{12})$ are projection operators for the symmetrical and skew parts respectively. Since P_{12} acts on a second order tensor to produce another of second order it must be a fourth order tensor. The unusual nature of this tensor is shown by considering the tetrad which is the direct product of two I

$$T = \mathsf{e}^r\mathsf{e}_r\mathsf{e}^s\mathsf{e}_s = II \tag{5.4.7}$$

T is the isotropic fourth order tensor, in the same sense as I is the isotropic second one, namely that its mixed components have the same numerical value in all coordinate systems. These components are

$$\delta^i_j\delta^m \tag{5.4.8}$$

and so T is symmetrical in its first pair of indices and also in its second pair. T can operate on a second order tensor, e.g. $\mathbf{e}_i\mathbf{e}_k$ to produce another tensor in three and only three different ways which are

$$\text{(i)} \qquad \mathbf{e}^r\mathbf{e}_r\,\mathbf{e}^s\mathbf{e}_s = \mathbf{e}^r\mathbf{e}_r\,g_{ik}$$
$$\cdot\,\cdot$$
$$\mathbf{e}_i\mathbf{e}_k$$

$$\text{(ii)} \qquad \mathbf{e}^r\mathbf{e}_r\,\mathbf{e}^s\mathbf{e}_s = \mathbf{e}_i\mathbf{e}_k$$
$$\cdot \quad \cdot$$
$$\mathbf{e}_i \quad \mathbf{e}_k$$

$$\text{(iii)} \qquad \mathbf{e}^r\mathbf{e}_r\,\mathbf{e}^s\mathbf{e}_s = \mathbf{e}_k\mathbf{e}_i$$
$$\cdot \quad \cdot$$
$$\mathbf{e}_k \quad \mathbf{e}_i$$

From these it follows that, for a general tensor with components a^{ik}, the three isotropic possibilities produce,

$$\text{(i)} \qquad (a^i{}_i)I$$
$$\text{(ii)} \qquad a^{ik}\mathbf{e}_i\mathbf{e}_k$$
$$\text{(iii)} \qquad a^{ik}\mathbf{e}_k\mathbf{e}_i$$

The first of these is the unit tensor with the trace of A as coefficient, the second is just A itself and the third is just P_{12} acting on A. The fact that the most general isotropic relation is a linear combination of these three operators is used in the theory of the elastic constants and elsewhere.

The symmetry properties of third order tensors are more complicated. A third order tensor which is symmetric with respect to each pair of indices is called fully symmetric, and fully skew if it is similarly skew. The fully symmetric part of an arbitrary tensor a_{ijk} is

$$\begin{aligned} b_{ijk} &= (1 + P_{12} + P_{23} + P_{31} + P_{123} + P_{132})a_{ijk} \\ &= (a_{ijk} + a_{jik} + a_{ikj} + a_{kji} + a_{jki} + a_{kij}) \end{aligned}$$

and the fully skew part is

$$\begin{aligned} c_{ijk} &= (1 - P_{12} - P_{23} - P_{31} + P_{123} + P_{132})a_{ijk} \\ &= (a_{ijk} - a_{jik} - a_{ikj} - a_{kji} + a_{jki} + a_{kij}) \end{aligned}$$

but four other types are needed before a_{ijk} can be expressed as their sum. A full discussion requires the theory of the permutation group.

5.5 Rotation of Axes

Many different kinds of transformation are included in the transformation of basis vectors envisaged in the transformation of a tensor and described by the matrix t_i^k. Among these one kind is of special significance. It is distinguished by the fact that it leaves the relative angles and lengths of the basis vectors unaltered and so may be regarded as a rotation of the basis though in a generalized sense. These angles and lengths are summed up in the metric matrix g_{ik} and the condition that they should be left invariant by t_i^r is that

$$g_{ik} = g_{rs} t_i^r t_k^s \tag{5.5.1}$$

When the basis system is orthonormal the metric is

$$g_{ik} = \delta_{ik} \tag{5.5.2}$$

and the condition that the transformed basis should also be orthonormal is

$$\delta_{ik} = t_i^r t_k^r \tag{5.5.3}$$

This means that t_i^r is an orthogonal matrix. By taking determinants of (3), it follows that

$$|t_i^r| = \pm 1 \tag{5.5.4}$$

Thus, for an orthonormal basis, the rotations are divided into two classes, the proper rotations which have $|t_i^r| = 1$ and correspond to physical rotations in the appropriate number of dimensions, and the improper rotations which have $|t_i^r| = -1$ and are reflections, inversions, etc.

These formulae need some amendment when more general spaces are considered. Thus when the components are complex numbers the metric matrix is defined as

$$g_{ik} = (\mathbf{e}_i^* \cdot \mathbf{e}_k) \tag{5.5.5}$$

and the condition that an orthonormal basis should transform into an orthonormal basis is that the transformation matrix should be unitary. The importance of orthogonal and unitary transformations in chemistry is due to the fact that they leave a sphere invariant and so govern the form of atomic wavefunctions.

5.6 Rotation Properties of Tensors

Tensors can be classified according to their order and their symmetry. When the basis is orthonormal and its transformations restricted to rotations the behaviour of tensors under transformation is easier to analyse and further classification is possible. It is convenient to consider a two-dimensional space in more detail since the general form of the results can then be demonstrated without elaborate analysis.

Since the bases are orthonormal the distinction between covariant and contravariant components can again be ignored.

In a two-dimensional space the components of a vector, with respect to an orthonormal basis, transform under rotation according to

$$\begin{aligned}\bar{x}_1 &= x_1 \cos \theta + x_2 \sin \theta \\ \bar{x}_2 &= -x_1 \sin \theta + x_2 \cos \theta\end{aligned} \tag{5.6.1}$$

This implies the orthogonal transformation matrix

$$t_i^{\,k} = \begin{pmatrix} \cos \theta & \sin \theta \\ -\sin \theta & \cos \theta \end{pmatrix} \tag{5.6.2}$$

The transformation law for a second order tensor requires two of these matrices. It takes a simple form when the tensor is skew. In matrix notation the transformation is written

$$\begin{aligned}\bar{c}_{rs} &= t_r^{\,i}\, c_{ij}\, t_s^{\,j} \\ &= \begin{pmatrix} \cos \theta & \sin \theta \\ -\sin \theta & \cos \theta \end{pmatrix} \begin{pmatrix} c_{11} & c_{12} \\ c_{21} & c_{22} \end{pmatrix} \begin{pmatrix} \cos \theta & -\sin \theta \\ \sin \theta & \cos \theta \end{pmatrix}\end{aligned} \tag{5.6.3}$$

and, using the skew relations, this reduces to

$$\bar{c}_{rs} = \begin{pmatrix} 0 & c_{12} \\ -c_{12} & 0 \end{pmatrix} = c_{rs} \tag{5.6.4}$$

On the other hand the improper rotation

$$t_i^{\,k} = \begin{pmatrix} \cos \theta & \sin \theta \\ \sin \theta & -\cos \theta \end{pmatrix} \tag{5.6.5}$$

leads to

$$\bar{c}_{rs} = -c_{rs} \tag{5.6.6}$$

Thus the skew tensor is invariant under rotation and changes sign under improper rotation. The symmetric tensor can be similarly transformed to give

$$\left.\begin{aligned}\bar{b}_{11} &= b_{11} \cos^2 \theta + b_{22} \sin^2 \theta + 2b_{12} \sin \theta \cos \theta \\ \bar{b}_{12} &= \bar{b}_{21} = (b_{22} - b_{11}) \sin \theta \cos \theta + b_{12}(\cos^2 \theta - \sin^2 \theta) \\ \bar{b}_{22} &= b_{11} \sin^2 \theta + b_{22} \cos^2 \theta - 2b_{12} \sin \theta \cos \theta\end{aligned}\right\} \tag{5.6.7}$$

In this transformation the trace remains invariant

$$\bar{b}_{11} + \bar{b}_{22} = b_{11} + b_{22} \tag{5.6.8}$$

so it is convenient to divide up the tensor into a part involving this trace and a remainder whose trace is zero. This is done by the change of variables

$$\begin{aligned} u &= b_{11} + b_{22} \;\;; & \bar{u} &= \bar{b}_{11} + \bar{b}_{22} \\ v &= \tfrac{1}{2}(b_{11} - b_{22}); & \bar{v} &= \tfrac{1}{2}(\bar{b}_{11} - \bar{b}_{22}) \\ w &= b_{12} \;\;; & \bar{w} &= \bar{b}_{12}\end{aligned} \tag{5.6.9}$$

so that (7) becomes

$$\bar{u} = u \tag{5.6.10}$$

$$\begin{pmatrix} \bar{v} \\ \bar{w} \end{pmatrix} = \begin{pmatrix} \cos 2\theta & \sin 2\theta \\ -\sin 2\theta & \cos 2\theta \end{pmatrix} \begin{pmatrix} v \\ w \end{pmatrix} \tag{5.6.11}$$

and the tensor is written as

$$b_{rs} = \begin{pmatrix} \frac{1}{2}u & 0 \\ 0 & \frac{1}{2}u \end{pmatrix} + \begin{pmatrix} v & w \\ w & -v \end{pmatrix} \tag{5.6.12}$$

An entity, such as the trace u, which is completely invariant is referred to, in group theory, as one of type Σ_1 while one, such as the skew tensor, which is invariant under proper rotations and changes sign under improper ones is of type Σ_2. A vector with two components such as x_i is of type Π and the two components of the trace-less symmetric tensor, transforming according to (11), are of type Δ. The most general second order tensor can, therefore, be split up into three parts of types Σ_1, Σ_2 and Δ.

This direct form of argument can be extended to third and higher order tensors but it soon becomes too complicated. The general results can be established more elegantly either by using a complex transformation to simplify the equations or by invoking the representation theory of the two-dimensional rotation group.

In three dimensions there are results of a similar type. A skew second order tensor has three independent components and these transform like a vector under proper rotations but with an additional change of sign when the rotation is improper. For this reason it is often called a pseudo-vector or an axial vector and has the label P' whereas the vector is labelled P. The trace of a symmetric second order tensor is again invariant and so can be separated from the remaining trace-less part. These are labelled S and D respectively. Thus, for example, the direct product of two vectors is a second order tensor. The trace of this tensor is their scalar product, its skew part is their vector product (which is a pseudo-vector) and the D part may be called their anisotropic product. In the theory of atomic structure this example is summarized symbolically as

$$(P)^2 = S + P' + D \tag{5.6.13}$$

5.7 Quadratic and Bilinear Forms

If a_{ik} are the covariant components of a second order tensor and x^i the contravariant components of an arbitrary vector then the quadratic form

$$f = a_{ik}x^i x^k \tag{5.7.1}$$

is a scalar though its value is a function of the x^i. Because of the double summation only the symmetrical part of the tensor contributes to f. If a_{ik} is not symmetrical it is better to consider the bilinear form

$$a_{ik}x^i y^k \tag{5.7.2}$$

These forms can be used to display tensor properties in geometrical terms. In two dimensions, for example, the vectors for which f is constant lie on a conic and, in three dimensions, the corresponding locus is a quadric.

When the basis is transformed the expression for f becomes

$$f = \bar{a}_{ik}\,\bar{x}^i\,\bar{x}^k \tag{5.7.3}$$

where

$$x^i = t^i{}_k\,\bar{x}^k \tag{5.7.4}$$

and

$$\bar{a}_{ik} = t^r{}_i\,a_{rs}\,t^s{}_k \tag{5.7.5}$$

or, in matrix notation,

$$\bar{\boldsymbol{A}} = \tilde{\boldsymbol{T}}\boldsymbol{A}\boldsymbol{T} \tag{5.7.6}$$

This transformation can be used to find the simplest expression for f but in most applications there are restrictions on the allowed transformations. Thus, if the original basis is orthonormal, it is usual for the transformation to be a rotation and the matrix $\boldsymbol{T}$ is orthogonal,

$$\boldsymbol{I} = \tilde{\boldsymbol{T}}\boldsymbol{T} \tag{5.7.7}$$

so that the formula for the length of a vector remains the same

$$|\boldsymbol{x}|^2 = \sum_i (x^i)^2 = \sum_r (\bar{x}^r)^2 \tag{5.7.8}$$

If $\boldsymbol{T}$ is the matrix of normalized eigencolumns of the real symmetric matrix $\boldsymbol{A}$ then $\boldsymbol{T}$ is orthogonal and the matrix $\boldsymbol{A}$ is diagonalized for, if

$$\boldsymbol{A}\boldsymbol{T} = \boldsymbol{T}\Lambda \tag{5.7.9}$$

where Λ is the diagonal matrix of eigenvalues

$$\Lambda = \ulcorner \lambda_1, \lambda_2, \ldots, \lambda_n \lrcorner \tag{5.7.10}$$

then

$$\tilde{\boldsymbol{T}}\boldsymbol{A}\boldsymbol{T} = \Lambda \tag{5.7.11}$$

and the quadratic form becomes a sum of squares

$$f = \sum_r \lambda_r (\bar{x}^r)^2 \tag{5.7.12}$$

On the other hand, there are many important applications in which the original basis is not orthogonal, so that the metric formula is

$$l^2 = g_{ik}x^i x^k \tag{5.7.13}$$

but the final basis is orthonormal and has

$$l^2 = \sum_i (\bar{x}^i)^2 \tag{5.7.14}$$

This requires a generalization of the definition of eigenvalues and eigenvectors to include the solutions of the equations

$$(a_{ik} - \lambda g_{ik})t^k = 0 \tag{5.7.15}$$

or

$$\boldsymbol{AT} = \boldsymbol{GT}\Lambda \tag{5.7.16}$$

where $\boldsymbol{T}$ is the matrix of generalized eigencolumns and Λ the diagonal matrix of generalized eigenvalues. The generalized orthogonality conditions (c.f. p. 85) and the normalization can be summarized as

$$\tilde{\boldsymbol{T}}\boldsymbol{GT} = \boldsymbol{I} \tag{5.7.17}$$

and this ensures (11) and (12). The quadratic form then becomes

$$f = \sum_r \lambda_r (\bar{x}^r)^2 \tag{5.7.18}$$

When complex numbers are involved these equations need amendment. The Hermitian form is

$$f = a_{ik}(x^i)^* x^k \tag{5.7.19}$$

where a_{ik} is Hermitian and, if the bases are orthonormal, $\boldsymbol{T}$ must be unitary. The final results are almost identical.

One illustration of this theory is in the theory of molecular vibration. The potential energy of vibration is a quadratic form in the variables which describe the distortion of the molecule from its equilibrium configuration and plays the role of the form f. The kinetic energy is also a quadratic form in these variables and plays the role of l^2. The new basis vectors are the normal modes of vibration with the property that both the kinetic energy and potential energy are sums of squares in the corresponding new variables x^i. The equations to be solved are generally of the form (15) and the eigenvalues are the squares of the normal frequencies.

5.8 Generalized Taylor Expansions

One of the common ways in which tensors arise in chemical problems is in the expansion of a scalar function, such as an energy or entropy, in terms of some variables. These can be discussed by a generalization of the Taylor expansion to n variables. If V is a function of the contravariant variables x^i then its expansion about the origin is

$$V(x^i) = V(0) + V_i x^i + \tfrac{1}{2} V_{ik} x^i x^k + \tfrac{1}{6} V_{ikl} x^i x^k x^l + \dots \quad (5.8.1)$$

where

$$V_i = \left(\frac{\partial V}{\partial x^i}\right)_{x^i=0} \quad (5.8.2)$$

$$V_{ik} = \left(\frac{\partial^2 V}{\partial x^i \partial x^k}\right)_{x^i=0} \quad (5.8.3)$$

$$V_{ikl} = \left(\frac{\partial^3 V}{\partial x^i \partial x^k \partial x^l}\right)_{x^i=0} \quad (5.8.4)$$

The fact that these derivatives transform covariantly is easily proved. It is usually true that V varies sufficiently smoothly with x^i that all these derivatives exist and are well-behaved at $x^i = 0$. It follows then that the tensors of all orders in (1) are fully symmetrical. The components of these tensors become properties of the system. For example, if V is the energy and x^i are the components of the electric field then V_i are the components of the dipole moment and V_{ik} of the polarizability.

In many applications these tensors are divided up further as in 5.6 and in 5.7. The quadratic form can be diagonalized by a suitable rotation of the basis. In three dimensions, for example, the tensor is specified by the three angles, which describe the directions of the eigenvectors, and the three eigenvalues. This diagonal matrix can be divided into its trace multiplied by the unit matrix and a traceless matrix. If the eigenvalues of the original matrix are $\lambda_1 \lambda_2 \lambda_3$ then, by definition, the trace is

$$\lambda_1 + \lambda_2 + \lambda_3 \quad (5.8.5)$$

The quantity

$$2\lambda_3 - (\lambda_1 + \lambda_2) \quad (5.8.6)$$

is often used as a measure of this trace-less tensor and called the anisotropy since it measures the departure of the original tensor from spherical symmetry while

$$(\lambda_1 - \lambda_2)/\lambda_3 \quad (5.8.7)$$

is a measure of its departure from axial symmetry.

EXERCISES

1. If $\sum_i u^i\, v(i)$ is an invariant, independent of the basis, where u^i are the contravariant components of an arbitrary vector, prove that the $v(i)$ must be the covariant components of a vector.

2. If a basis system has
$$g_{ik} = \begin{pmatrix} 1 & 2 & 1 \\ 2 & 4 & 3 \\ 1 & 3 & 5 \end{pmatrix}$$
and a certain tensor has mixed components
$$a_i{}^k = \begin{pmatrix} 0 & 1 & 0 \\ 2 & 1 & 0 \\ 2 & 1 & -1 \end{pmatrix}$$
prove that it is symmetrical.

3. If c_{ik} are the covariant components of a tensor and x^k the contravariant components of a vector prove that $c_{ik}x^k$ transforms as the covariant components of a vector.

4. The tensor ε_{ijk} is defined in a three dimensional space by the conditions
$$\begin{aligned} \varepsilon_{ijk} &= 1 \text{ when } ijk \text{ is even permutation of } 1\ 2\ 3 \\ &= -1 \text{ when } ijk \text{ is odd permutation of } 1\ 2\ 3 \\ &= 0 \text{ otherwise} \end{aligned}$$
Prove that
(i) it is fully skew
(ii) its transformation equations become
$$\varepsilon_{ijk} = |t_l{}^m|\ \varepsilon_{ijk}$$
(iii) the components of the vector product of two vectors defined in terms of their contravariant components as $(a^2b^3-a^3b^2,\ a^3b^1-a^1b^3,\ a^1b^2-a^2b^1)$ transform covariantly.

5. Show that the tensor, whose components are
$$a_i{}^k = \begin{pmatrix} a & b \\ c & d \end{pmatrix}$$
cannot possess more than two independent invariants of the type $a_i{}^i$, $a_i{}^k a_k{}^i$, $a_i{}^k\, a_k{}^l\, a_l{}^i, \ldots$. Show also that this can be generalized to n dimensions.

6. Show that $ax^2 + 2hxy + by^2$ can be expressed as a square $(\boldsymbol{\alpha}x + \boldsymbol{\beta}y)^2$ if $\boldsymbol{\alpha}$ is a multiple of $\begin{pmatrix} 1 & 0 \\ 0 & -1 \end{pmatrix}$ and $\boldsymbol{\beta}$ depends on $\begin{pmatrix} 1 & 0 \\ 0 & 1 \end{pmatrix}$ and $\begin{pmatrix} 0 & 1 \\ 1 & 0 \end{pmatrix}$.

7. Verify that
$$t_i{}^l = \begin{pmatrix} 1 & -2 \\ 1 & -1 \end{pmatrix}$$
is a generalized rotation which preserves the metric
$$g_{ik} = \begin{pmatrix} 2 & 1 \\ 1 & 1 \end{pmatrix}$$

8. Show that the transformation
$$t_i{}^k = \begin{pmatrix} \cosh\theta & \sinh\theta \\ \sinh\theta & \cosh\theta \end{pmatrix}$$
where θ is arbitrary, preserves the metric
$$g_i{}^l = \begin{pmatrix} 1 & 0 \\ 0 & -1 \end{pmatrix}$$

9. If a_{ik} is skew prove that

$$c_{ijk} = a_{ij}\, b_k + a_{jk}\, b_i + a_{ki}\, b_j$$

is fully skew.

10. The set of all polynomials in x of degree not greater than three form a vector space and the scalar product of two polynomials $p(x)$, $q(x)$ can be defined as

$$p \cdot q = \int_{-1}^{1} p(x)\, q(x)\, \mathrm{d}x$$

Prove that

(i) $1, x, x^2, x^3$ form a basis in this space and find the reciprocal basis

(ii) the effect of the operator $\mathrm{d}/\mathrm{d}x$ on a polynomial is equivalent to a second order tensor in the vector space and find its mixed components.

11. Expand $\{(x - \bar{x})^2 + (y - \bar{y})^2 + (z - \bar{z})^2\}^{-\frac{1}{2}}$ as a Taylor series in $(\bar{x}, \bar{y}, \bar{z})$ and show how the first terms can be interpreted in terms of tensors and in terms of associated Legendre functions.

FOR FURTHER READING

The more elementary textbooks are listed first.

Chapter 1

Hague, B. *An Introduction to Vector Analysis*, Methuen, London 1939.
Rutherford, D. E. *Vector Methods*, Oliver & Boyd, Edinburgh 1943.
Weatherburn, C. E. *Elementary Vector Analysis*, Bell, London 1931.

Chapter 2

Frazer, R. A., Duncan, W. J. and Coller, A. R. *Elementary Matrices*, Cambridge University Press, Cambridge 1938.
Ferrar, W. L. *Algebra*, Clarendon Press, Oxford 1941.
Ferrar, W. L. *Finite Matrices*, Clarendon Press, Oxford 1951.
Birkhoff, G. and MacLane, S. *A Survey of Modern Algebra*, MacMillan. New York 1953.

Chapter 3

Faddeeva, V. N. *Computational Methods of Linear Algebra*, Dover, New York 1959.
Bodewig, E. *Matrix Calculus*, North-Holland, Amsterdam 1959.
Löwdin, P. O. Quantum theory of cohesive properties of solids, *Advances in Physics* 1956, **5**, 1.

Chapter 4

As under chapter 2 together with
Bodewig, E. *Matrix Calculus*, North-Holland, Amsterdam 1959.
Householder, A. S. *Principles of Numerical Analysis*, McGraw-Hill, New York 1953.
Paige, L. J. and Taussky, O. (Ed.). *Simultaneous Linear Equations and the Determination of Eigenvalues* (3 vols), N.B.S. (Nos. 29, 39, 49) Washington 1953–5.
Weyl, H. *The Theory of Groups and Quantum Mechanics*, Methuen, London 1931.
Turnbull, H. W. *The Theory of Determinants, Matrices and Invariants* (3rd ed.), Dover, New York 1960.
Löwdin, P. O. Correlation in quantum mechanics, *Adv. in Chem. Phys.* 1959, **2**, 207.

Chapter 5

Temple, G. *Cartesian Tensors*, Methuen, London 1960.
Weyl, H. *Space, Time and Matter*, Methuen, London 1930.
Halmos, P. R. *Finite-dimensional Vector Spaces*, van Nostrand, Princeton, 1958.

INDEX